CURIOUS FOOTPRINTS

For the Sunderland Library —

may Prof. Hitchcock

bring you inspiration —

Edward Hitchcock, painted about 1840 by the German-born artist William Rohner.
Courtesy of Mead Art Museum, Amherst College.

CURIOUS FOOTPRINTS:

Professor Hitchcock's

Dinosaur Tracks & Other Natural History

Treasures at Amherst College

≫ ≪

TEXT *by Nancy Pick*

PHOTOGRAPHS *by Frank Ward*

AFTERWORD *by Ben Lifson*

AMHERST COLLEGE PRESS

For my husband, Lawrence, and my boychiks, Jacob and Milo. — N. P.

For my wife, Vivian, and my children, Tobey and Caleb. — F. W.

FIRST EDITION

Front cover: Tracks of *Brontozoum validum*, one of the Pioneer Valley's largest dinosaurs.

Back cover: Noah's Raven slab, the world's first documented fossil footprints, discovered
about 1802. The tracks were made by *Anomoepus scambus*, a small ornithischian, or "bird-
hipped," dinosaur.

Printed by Thames Printing Co. Inc.,
Norwich, CT

Book Design by Su Auerbach

ISBN 0-943184-09-6

CONTENTS

Marble bust of Edward Hitchcock, made about 1865 by Irish-born sculptor Martin Milmore. Photographed in the Track Room of the old Pratt Museum.

PROFESSOR HITCHCOCK'S PECULIAR BIRD OBSESSION:
A BIOGRAPHICAL SKETCH
By Nancy Pick

Dear Professor Hitchcock,

I write to you from the future. You died nearly one hundred and fifty years ago, and I hope your soul reached heaven. As for your body, it has broken down into chemical elements, scattered by the winds and the waves. Possibly, as you suggested, these elements have become parts of other people. Perhaps even me.

I confess I find myself drawn to you. You were brilliant. From the backwater of Amherst, you established a reputation even in London. And yet you were vulnerable, a little tortured, often endearingly wrong. In trying to unravel you, I have read your scientific papers, your books, your letters, your poems, your lectures, your travel journals, your diary, even your love notes. In certain ways, you would be pleased by my biographer's gaze. You longed to be remembered. But in other ways you would find me unsuited to the task, for reasons I will soon make clear.

As a physical presence, you were strong, and handsome. You hiked thousands of miles, up every mountain in Massachusetts, wielding your geologist's hammer. You dressed well, perhaps anxious to convince the world that you were no mere bumpkin. In my favorite portrait, you wear an elegant topcoat with a fur collar (was it beaver?) and a pinched waist. Your passport, as translated from the French, described you this way:

> Height: 5 feet 11 inches
> Forehead: High
> Eyes: Blue
> Nose: A bit big [*un peu grand*]

Well, I would call it a Roman nose, long but not unappealing.

Now you must forgive me, for there are aspects of my twenty-first-century culture that you will find unsettling. You lived during the early Victorian age, a time famous for its repression. These days, we tend to read sex into everything. And though you were never one to deny human desires — and your dear wife gave birth eight times — still you would not approach texts with the wink that we do. And so when I read this passage about you, from the Reverend William Tyler's eulogy, I can only conclude that you projected a certain *energy*:

Every bone and sinew was alive with sensibility. Every organ thrilled to its extremity with the excitement of his mind, when it was roused to action; every nerve and fibre of his body quivered with pain or pleasure, as his heart sank with sadness or leaped for joy within him.

I find this terribly attractive. Yet as you know only too well, such extreme sensitivity had its drawbacks. You suffered from lifelong dyspepsia, a Victorian affliction of rattled nerves and troubled digestion. For years you allowed yourself little more sustenance than bread, butter, milk, and a jelled concoction made from arrowroot. (I made it once and found it shockingly inedible.)

But now let us turn to a weightier matter, the question of your posterity. I am happy to report that your name does indeed live on. More than two centuries after your birth, you are known as a pioneering geologist and "dinosaur hunter." You continue to appear in articles and books on the history of geology. Also, you are linked to a poet you knew in her youth, who became famous after death: Emily Dickinson. Your influence appears in her intimate knowledge of nature, from botany to birds.

You did, I suspect, note my use above of the word *dinosaur*. I'm afraid that, concerning your reputation, there are matters less cheerful to discuss — and I can only hope you've kept your sense of humor. I must tell you that most of your strongest convictions turned out to be mistaken. You were wrong to doubt the existence of an Ice Age. You were wrong to deny the theory of evolution. And, most painful of all, you were wrong about the animals that made your beloved fossil footprints. They were not gigantic ancient birds after all, but dinosaurs.

Moreover, your entire intellectual framework has fallen into disfavor. You made a heroic attempt to reconcile science and Christianity, even as new discoveries rendered that effort ever more challenging. But Charles Darwin turned out to be right. And with the success of his theory, God departed from the natural world, yielding to the cruel mechanism of survival of the fittest. Here in the twenty-first century, science has become a secular pursuit, at least among the educated. And if "intelligent design" has made a comeback in recent years, I'm afraid the notion lacks any scientific foundation whatsoever.

In truth, I am pleased that you were not a pure skeptic — if such a person even existed in your pious age. I find endlessly fascinating your struggle to make the Bible fit the latest science. It appeals to the student of literature in me, or even of Talmud. (There, I've done it, I've dropped a hint.) People may assume that you took the Bible literally, but that is anything but true. Instead, you split hairs and turned hermeneutic somersaults to maintain the Bible's relevance to the scientific world.

Before ending this letter, I ought to explain my connections to you, for there are many. I am a graduate of your college, the institution you saved from bankruptcy and served so admirably as president. You are puzzled, perhaps. But Amherst College has accepted women students since 1975, and I arrived just four years later. I think you are not displeased, however, as you were a great believer in women receiving higher education. And my Amherst ties run deeper than my own education, for my father is also an alumnus, and by a quirk of fate my husband is a professor there as well.

My ties to you are also geographical. I live in Sunderland, in a farmhouse you might recognize, for it was built in 1804, while you were still a child, living in the next town over. Out my back window is Mount Sugarloaf, which you climbed often and longed to rename something less prosaic. I have a view, too, of the Connecticut River, whose contours you so carefully examined. Just up the river is the site where, not yet a scientist, you discovered specimens of fossilized fish. And along the banks to the north and south lie the sandstone slabs in which you found the ancient footprints that made your reputation.

But here's the difficult part, dear Professor. I'm afraid your college is no longer in the hands of Congregationalists, or evangelical Christians of any sort. The transformation you feared has taken place, and Amherst is now a secular place, welcoming people of many colors and creeds. You asked your heirs to strip your fossil collections from the college if ever it fell into un-Christian hands. In the end, they chose not to follow your directive. Times change, Professor Hitchcock, and America is now a place of immense diversity.

As for me, I am what you would have called a "Hebrew"— I am Jewish. This may sit uncomfortably with you, I realize. Although you studied the Hebrew language in your scholarly pursuits, I find no record that you ever made the acquaintance of actual Jews. Whatever your misgivings, I hope you can tolerate my attentions, which are nothing if not admiring.

In the essay that follows I intend to lay out the highlights of your scientific endeavors, with various asides designed to reveal the complexities of your character. Death was never far from your thoughts, even from a tender age. Yet you lived fully seventy years and seemed to feel, observe, ponder, and accomplish enough for several lifetimes.

With great respect and regard, pray believe me, dear Professor,
Yours faithfully and obliged,

In the thousands of pages he left behind, Edward Hitchcock never said why. Why was he anti-dinosaur? Why did he insist, unto death, that his beloved fossil footprints were made by gigantic ancient birds? He was willing to imagine birds with bony tails, even birds with four legs. But in his mind, they were still *birds*. He refused to besmirch them with the term *saurian*, the Victorian word for dinosaur.

The explanation for his bird obsession remains something of a mystery. I know Hitchcock quite intimately, as well as one can know a person who lived in a different century. I know what he ate, and whom he loved, and how he was tormented. I can even read his impossible handwriting. Yet the professor provided few direct clues to his anti-dinosaur attitude in either his vast published writings, or in the personal diary he kept for more than thirty years. His insistence on birds remains as mysterious as Hitchcock himself, a man sensual but pious, imaginative but meticulous, brilliant, bigoted, powerful, neurotic, workaholic, loving, whimsical, wrongheaded, dyspeptic, poetic, infuriating, and staggeringly charming.

It is my task, in this essay, to tease out answers. I will pore over his life and his career, seeking hints to his bird stance in his science, his Christian piety, and his psychology. There will be diversions along the way, to note aspects of Hitchcock too delightful to pass by, including his phrenology report, his love letters, his zoological temperance meeting, and his essential (and surprising) feminism.

If his bird theory was initially met with skepticism, Hitchcock did enjoy moments of sweet triumph. The discovery of the moa, the enormous extinct bird of New Zealand, gave his thesis a great boost. So did fossilized feces, which he proudly sent to British experts. But by the end of his life, his bird concept was once again, as he put it, "tossed on the sea of difficulty."[1]

Still, Hitchcock's influence should not be underestimated. Charles Lyell, the renowned Scottish geologist, traveled to Amherst expressly to meet him and see the footprints. Richard Owen, the British anatomist who coined the word *dinosaur*, kept up a correspondence with Hitchcock from London. (Both men felt frustrated by the lack of fossil bones in the Connecticut Valley, which might have settled the question of the track makers' identity.) Charles Darwin himself, in a letter to Hitchcock, called the footprints "one of the most curious discoveries of the present century."[2]

Despite his brilliance and his international reputation, Hitchcock fell short of being the kind of genius who could transcend his era. Nearly every word he wrote appears obsolete from our vantage point, some hundred and fifty years after his death. Certainly, he was wrong to believe that his Connecticut Valley fossil footprints had been made by ancient birds.

Or was he?

In 1835, when Hitchcock saw his first fossil footprints, he concluded that they had been made by enormous ancient birds. His bird thesis was the simplest and most obvious explanation. Already, casual observers had called the footprints "turkey tracks," for they did indeed resemble the footprints of those familiar creatures. Hitchcock may well have thought that birds presented the most elegant solution to the paleontological mystery.[4] Yet it is important to note that, at the time, the word *dinosaur* had not even been coined. Hitchcock went on to defend his bird theory for the next thirty years, even as dinosaur science made tremendous advances. He stuck by his idea despite many harsh challenges, and was rewarded with respect and even occasional vindication.

Hitchcock never claimed to have discovered the Connecticut Valley footprints, but instead insisted that he was the first to describe them for science. A local physician, James Deane, initially brought the footprints to his attention. Although this seemed a generous act, Deane soon decided that he wanted his own share of footprint glory, ultimately becoming Hitchcock's bitter rival. (Hitchcock's claim to footprint fame was eventually sustained, but not without a battle.)

According to Hitchcock, the first footprints he saw had been noted by one W. W. Draper of Greenfield, Massachusetts. The story goes that, while walking home from church in March of 1835, Draper passed by the home of William Wilson, where in front of the house were lying flagstone slabs for a new sidewalk. After examining them, Draper remarked to Wilson, "Here are some turkey tracks made 3,000 years ago."[5] Wilson then

Six Major Accomplishments of Edward Hitchcock (1793–1864)[3]

Established the science of Ichnology, the study of trace fossils — including footprints, excrement, and eggs.

Amassed the world's largest collection of dinosaur footprints, with some 10,000 individual impressions. Also collected 10,000 impressions left by other animals, and by plants.

Wrote one of the first authentically American geology textbooks, used for thirty years in colleges across the country.

Saved Amherst College from bankruptcy and established it as a place of scientific excellence.

Made an accurate geologic map of Massachusetts, only the second state geologic map in the country.

Mapped the contours of an important geological feature, later named Glacial Lake Hitchcock.

showed them to Deane, who in turn wrote a letter describing them to Hitchcock, the region's most prominent geologist. Deane called them "the tracks of a turkey in relief."[6]

Hitchcock was initially dismissive. As state geologist, he knew that certain structures in sedimentary rocks could resemble footprints.[7] Besides, the only confirmed fossil tracks had been found in Scotland, apparently those of an ancient tortoise. Deane persisted, however, and sent Hitchcock plaster casts of the footprints. With that evidence before him, Hitchcock's eyes were opened. He made a trip up to Greenfield to see the tracks firsthand — and from that moment, at the age of forty-two, became a man obsessed. He spent the summer combing the Connecticut Valley for evidence of tracks. He found them in the sidewalks of Deerfield and Northampton, then traced the flagstones to local quarries, where he found more fossil tracks in the red sandstone, some very small and some, as he put it, "almost incredibly large."[8] The tracks generally showed the impressions of three front toes (and occasionally the hind toe also left an imprint).

An illustration showing the famous "Noah's Raven" footprint slab, shortly after its discovery in South Hadley, Massachusetts, about 1802. These were the first fossil footprints ever documented in America. The slab is now prominently displayed in Amherst College's natural history museum.

That summer, Hitchcock also identified the first documented fossil tracks in North America. About 1802, a youth named Pliny Moody was plowing his father's South Hadley field when he unearthed a sandstone slab bearing mysteriously large footprints. With typical Yankee frugality, he put it to good use as the family doorstep. Elihu Dwight of South Hadley later bought the slab, apparently as a conversation piece. Dwight called the tracks those of "Noah's Raven," perhaps in the belief that only a biblical bird could have had such impressive feet. Hitchcock eventually purchased the slab, which is now a centerpiece in Amherst College's new natural history museum.

At first, Hitchcock did indeed refer to the footprints as "turkey tracks."[9] Although he later erected a scientific edifice around his view, the bird idea seemed to have had for him an almost philosophical appeal. One modern scholar snidely remarked that the professor arrived at his bird thesis because "As a [Christian] fundamentalist, Hitchcock was accustomed to literal acceptance of folk beliefs."[10] This seems simplistic, for Hitchcock had legitimate scientific reasons for believing that the tracks were made by birds, as I will explore below. Yet there is perhaps some truth to the notion. Local quarrymen had long called the footprints "turkey tracks."[11] Certainly, it was far easier to imagine the track makers as birds than as such fundamentally bizarre creatures as dinosaurs.

Hitchcock rushed to get his discoveries into print. In January of 1836, he described in Yale's prestigious *American Journal of Science* seven new species of ancient bird track. The largest footprint, now called *Eubrontes giganteus*, led this usually sober man to use exclamation points. "The whole length of the foot…is sixteen or seventeen inches!" he wrote.[12] The length of its stride measured "between four and six feet!" He knew it was no mere turkey.

However huge, birds did seem the most plausible track makers. Although he felt that "the geologist should be the last of all men to trust to first impressions,"[13] he believed his careful investigations justified his initial conclusion. His paper includes, for purposes of comparison, drawings of the tracks of turkeys, chickens, geese, peahens, and snipe. He was particularly impressed by the tracks of snipe, which he had noticed in mud near the banks of the Connecticut River. If that mud were suddenly hardened into sandstone, he wrote, snipe tracks would be scarcely distinguishable from the fossilized ones. With this groundbreaking paper Hitchcock did not merely document his footprints. He

This large footprint, now called Eubrontes giganteus, *was described by Hitchcock in 1836, in his first publication on fossil tracks. He wrote, "The whole length of the foot…is sixteen or seventeen inches!"*

founded an entirely new scientific discipline: Ichnology, the study of plant and animal traces, including fossil footprints. (Originally, Hitchcock had called his science Ornithichnology, "the study of stony bird tracks." Happily, this was later clipped to its current form by the English geologist William Buckland.)

The tracks also fired Hitchcock's imagination. He published a poem, imagining his majestic sandstone bird — twenty feet tall — brought back to life. Appearing in the New York monthly magazine *The Knickerbocker*, the verse articulated the fervent desire of every paleontologist:

Bird of a former world! — would that thy form
Might reappear in these thy former haunts!

A sorceress then conjures up the bird, which rises out of the water and squawks, its huge neck resembling a "sawyer," or submerged log:

The waters suddenly leap'd toward the sky;
And up flew swiftly, what a sawyer seem'd,
But prov'd a bird's neck, with a frightful beak.
A huge-shaped body follow'd; stilted high,
As if two mainmasts propp'd it up. The bird
Of sandstone fame was truly come again;
And shaking his enormous plumes and wings,
And rolling his broad eye around, amaz'd,
He gave a yell so loud and savage too —
Though to *Iguanodons* and kindred tribes,
Music it might have seem'd — on human ear
It grated harshly…[14]

A very early and amusing image of Iguanodons, *from Gideon Mantell's 1838 book* The Wonders of Geology. *Mantell had named and described the dinosaur in 1825, based on teeth alone. Iguanodon was only the second dinosaur ever to be described.*

Hitchcock's mention of *Iguanodon* here is significant. He may have lived in the scientific backwater of Amherst, but he read all the latest geology. He knew that in England, fossil remains of three gigantic ancient reptiles had been identified, and his poem goes on to mention them: *Iguanodon*, *Hylaeosaurus*, and *Megalosaurus*. Not until 1842, six years after Hitchcock's poem appeared, would the great British anatomist Richard Owen name the suborder *Dinosauria*, from which the word *dinosaur* was created. As Owen envisioned them at the time, dinosaurs were fat, lumbering animals that stood heavily on four feet. Gideon

Mantell, another prominent English geologist, certainly did not offer a prettier picture. Mantell first described *Iguanodon* in 1825, initially relying on just a tooth, which, he noted, bore a striking resemblance to that of a modern-day iguana. Judging by an illustration from his 1838 book *The Wonders of Geology*, Mantell imagined *Iguanodons* as pudgy, googly-eyed alligators. Not surprisingly, Hitchcock found these "saurians" somewhat disappointing. He believed his ancient birds to be superior, imagining them as taller and smarter than the ancient reptiles. Indeed, he believed them "the most perfect animals that then existed."[15]

If Hitchcock found a certain nobility in his ancient birds, I believe he also clung to his bird theory out of sheer stubbornness. It was deep within his nature to fight for an idea once he had embraced it. It is, however, a measure of his complexity that his was not the usual type of stubbornness. Hitchcock exhibited a strange mix of pessimism and drive. As his diary states, "So feeble is the organ of hope in my cranium that I very rarely dare expect success in any important enterprise. And yet when I fairly take hold of it, I persevere with a tenacity that looks as if I was sanguine of success beyond all reason."[16]

⊰ LOVE ⊱

If stubbornness helps explain Hitchcock's devotion to his bird theory, so does another trait in his character: faithfulness. Of course, I cannot prove that he never had dalliances. He was certainly very close to Mary Lyon, founder of Mount Holyoke College. For that matter, his tombstone describes him as a "lover of men," a comment that would certainly be interpreted differently today. But judging from the way he wrote about his wife, Orra White Hitchcock, he felt toward her deep love and even "ardour."

The first evidence of their meeting dates from 1814, when Orra White played the lead in the youthful Edward's play, *Downfall of Bonaparte: A Tragedy*.[17] At the time he was twenty-one, living in his hometown of Deerfield, and independently studying science. In the spring of that year he had endured his own downfall. His greatest wish had been to study astronomy at Harvard, but a case of mumps had left his eyes weakened and painful. He never did attend college, a deficit that plagued him throughout his life.[18] The disappointment left him deeply depressed, and in his diary he explained that it was during this time that he began his religious conversion from mainstream Congregationalism to the "Orthodox" — or evangelical — branch. (Had he attended Harvard, he might have found himself pulled toward that college's Unitarianism. Instead, as a member of the Orthodox, he came to despise Harvard's religious liberalism.)

When she acted in her future husband's play, Orra White was eighteen, working as a preceptress and assistant teacher at Deerfield Academy. She instructed girls in painting, drawing, cartography, and, yes, astronomy. Orra painted elegant and scientifically accurate watercolors of botanical specimens, some of the most exquisite preserved in her notebook, *Herbarium Parvum Pictum*.

In 1818, publication of her sketch of Turners Falls made her one of the first published female illustrators in America.[19] If their courtship began in 1814, it was certainly lengthy. Perhaps Hitchcock needed to establish himself in a proper career before they could marry. He had no family money to fall back on, for his father was a poor hatter. In 1816, Hitchcock became principal of Deerfield Academy, a post he held for two years. Since that did not seem an adequate livelihood, he began studying for the ministry, spending several months at Yale. Orra held strong evangelical beliefs from the start, and apparently influenced Hitchcock to become an "Orthodox" Christian.

Roses and morning glories, somewhat fancifully depicted by Orra White Hitchcock. Courtesy of Archives and Special Collections, Amherst College Library.

Their courtship was not entirely puritanical.[20] Two love notes have survived, in the Amherst College archives. It is interesting that the family found these appropriate for preservation, as they are slightly racy. One note shows that Hitchcock was perfectly capable of plotting to see Orra. It suggests that they get together, on a May evening, at the house of a mutual friend, "where the eye of suspicion cannot perceive us."[21] Note his remarkable postscript, in which the word *interview* means meeting: "P.S. Be not in fear of another *all night interview*." (Lest you draw certain implications, be assured that their first child was not born until a year after they married.)

Here is another delightful note saved from their prenuptial days:

Do you think Orra, if you should go up to Harriet's toward night we could make it so muddy, dark and rainy this evening that it would be *impossible* for you to get back tonight? If such should be your belief I assure you I should be very happy to be placed in the same predicament (*after Mr. Eliphlalet & wife have gone to bed*) or in other words "I'll be with you bye & bye."

E.[22]

The informality of his signature is quite striking. Once married, he always signed his letters to her "Edward Hitchcock," probably with an eye toward posterity.[23]

They did not marry until 1824, when she was twenty-five and he twenty-eight. The couple endured terrible sadness in their early years, for their first child, a son named Edward, died shortly before his second birthday. Their second baby died at birth. All told, Orra endured eight pregnancies, giving birth to her last child at age

This painting, The Return of Professor Hitchcock, *shows the professor coming home to his family at 271 South Pleasant Street in Amherst, a house still standing today. Unsigned, the work was likely done by an itinerant portrait painter. Beside the house stands the octagon Hitchcock built as his "cabinet," for his collection of rocks and minerals. Courtesy of Mead Art Museum, Amherst College.*

forty-two. The remaining six children — four girls and two boys — all survived into adulthood. Mary, the eldest, illustrated one of her father's books. Edward Jr., known as "Doc," became a much-loved professor at Amherst College and a pioneer in the field of physical education. Charles taught at Dartmouth College. The youngest child, Emily Hitchcock Terry, was a gifted botanical illustrator and in 1992 the subject of a book describing her life and art.[24] (Ironically, no full-length biography of her distinguished father has ever been published.)

Remarkably enough, Orra's family and social responsibilities did not deter her from her artwork. She illustrated many of her husband's works, by his count producing some 232 full-page plates and more than 1,000 figures for texts. She also produced dozens of large sketches on canvas, including a geyser and a mastodon, for his classroom lectures. Whenever she could find the time, she accompanied Hitchcock on his geological excursions. She witnessed, for example, the exact moment in which a new oxbow was created by the overflowing Connecticut River.

Certainly, Hitchcock appreciated his exceptional spouse. In his diary, he wrote the following:

> With such a wife how delightful a place is home! Will it be called weakness if I confess that I never leave it for a week while she is left behind without experiencing dejection & homesickness: and I confess that this attraction has proved the greatest fear I have ever experienced in the prosecution of geological researches. The older I grow the more painful it is to break away from my family. For though nearly fifty years old I find that my affection for my wife has not lost the freshness, the ardour, nor even the enthusiasm of youth — How trying then must be the final separation! Oh this is almost the only earthly trial which I cannot think of with calmness! The idea unmans me...[25]

✄ DYSPEPSIA ✄

Given Hitchcock's sentimentality, it's hardly surprising that he felt repelled by creatures as monstrous as dinosaurs. Moreover, conjuring up dinosaurs, especially in the early days of paleontology, required a slightly overheated imagination. Hitchcock tried to maintain a more sober outlook. A temperance advocate, he rarely touched alcohol. Indeed, there were times in his life when he hardly ate. Twice he experienced visions while suffering from fevers,[26] but dinosaurs were not what came to mind.

As a strong yet acutely sensitive man, Hitchcock spent much of his life on a kind of roller coaster. At times he seemed indefatigable. In his late thirties, he crisscrossed the state of Massachusetts on foot and horseback, climbing its highest peaks and covering thousands of miles. But following this remarkable odyssey, his diary records that he suffered a terrible bout of "dyspepsia." Indigestion was his primary symptom, but not the only one. To the Victorians, dyspepsia also had a psychological dimension, typically manifested as anxiety and depression. Or, as Hitchcock put it, "unreasonable fears, despondency of mind, and dismal forebodings of evil."[27]

In the 1820s, Hitchcock conducted an exhaustive search of the medical litera-ture in hopes of improving both his digestion and his mood. Identifying three demons — alcohol, caffeine, and meat — he became a health-food zealot. He taught an entire course at Amherst College on the subject of dyspepsia and in 1830 published his lectures as a book, *Dyspepsy Forestalled & Resisted: or Lectures on Diet, Regimen, and Employment*. Immoderate eating and drinking, he posited, were to blame for "the premature prostration and early decay of students and profes-sional men."[28]

Always, he sought ways to improve his health, sometimes resorting to measures that seemed extreme. His geologic survey of the state began as a way to avoid depression. In his late thirties, he wrote in his diary, he believed he needed "some thorough & systematic course of exercise…to give more rigor to my constitution & to save me from sinking."[29] About 1829 he proposed the idea of a geologic survey to Massachusetts Governor Levi Lincoln. Lincoln liked the idea and pitched it to the state legislature. In June of 1830, Hitchcock received a paid

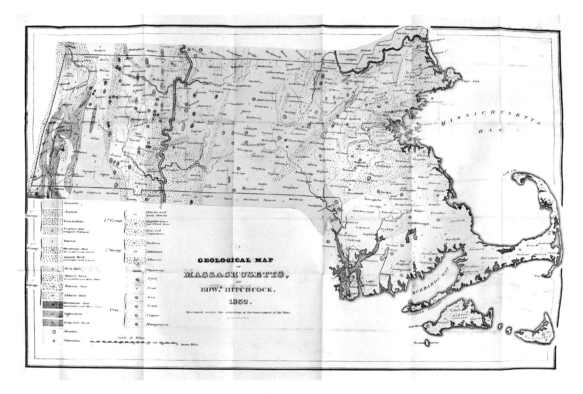

In 1832, Hitchcock created the first geologic map of Massachusetts. He covered nearly every inch of the state during his fieldwork, traveling some 5,000 miles by horse and on foot.

commission, becoming the first state geologist of Massachusetts. Records his diary, "I could not doubt but that this was an opening which Providence had made for me for the improvement of my health: and therefore I engaged in the business immediately & within two years have gone over nearly all the state & travelled probably not less than 5000 miles."[30] Who but Hitchcock would consider this getting "some exercise"?

During his journeys, he was abstemious indeed. "Not one drop of alcoholic liquor have I drunk during all my wanderings in almost all kind of weather," he wrote.[31] For that matter, he hardly touched tea or coffee. "Bread & milk have been my principal diet," he continued, "& using these moderately I have found myself

A Tale of Temperance

Hitchcock was a strong advocate of temperance at a time when the average American male drank half a pint of whiskey every day. Arguing his viewpoint with humor, he published in 1849 a small book, *History of a Zoological Temperance Convention, Held in Central Africa.* In it, the animals debate the pros and cons of alcohol. The testimony of the zebra offers some choice words about human conduct in bars:

HISTORY

OF A

ZOOLOGICAL

TEMPERANCE CONVENTION,

HELD IN CENTRAL AFRICA.

BY EDWARD HITCHCOCK, D. D., LL. D.

Ridentem dicere verum,
Quid vetat?   Horace.

FITCHBURG, MASS.:
PUBLISHED BY GEORGE TRASK.
1864.

> I have been in the dens of all sorts of animals, and have seen them in their worst moods, and I declare that I have never seen so filthy and disgusting a place as a bar-room, fitted up according to law, for the public good, yet filled with the steam of alcohol, the smoke of tobacco, and the wrangling and cursing of half-drunken men. If this is the civilization and refinement, which the gentlemen would introduce among the animals, deliver us, I say, deliver us from so awful a curse! Often as I have witnessed the effects of alcohol among men, I have exclaimed, "how thankful am I that my name is not *Homo sapiens*, but *Equus zebra*."[32]

equal to the most severe & long protracted labours & climbing the highest mountains — a thing which I could never have done had I used stimulating drink or much animal food."

In 1832 the professor published his state geologic map, in color. It is only the second state geologic map in the country, after North Carolina's. The map was well received and even today is considered an impressively accurate guide to the state's basic rock formations.

A year later, Hitchcock proudly saw his first book published, a thick tome titled *Report on the Geology, Mineralogy, Botany, and Zoology of Massachusetts*. The state printed 1,200 copies, providing one for every town and two for each of the state's colleges, Harvard, Williams, and Amherst. Nevertheless, he felt guilty about his worldly ambitions, confessing in his diary that such intensive scientific work had diverted him from religious devotion. "Strange that a study of the works of God should tend to make one forget God!"[33] The book was considered a major accomplishment, establishing his reputation as one of America's foremost geologists. Over the next several years, fully twenty states would follow his example, putting up public money to back their own geological surveys.[34] (In the 1850s, aided by his two sons, Hitchcock published the survey for Vermont.) These maps were not only educational but also useful for identifying mineral and ore deposits, and facilitating route planning for roads and canals.[35]

Only two years after his triumph, Hitchcock was a wreck — pale, feeble, and emaciated. His fieldwork done, he suffered a full-blown attack of dyspepsia: "Oh what a winter of suffering is this! Dreadful is the prostration of nervous energy which I endure. I thought I had known before nearly everything that could be known of the horrors of dyspepsy. But I had scarcely entered the vestibule of this inquisitor's torturing house."[36] Some blamed his prostration on the limitations of his diet. Tired of his attacks on their indulgent life-styles, they may have viewed his decline as a kind of sweet justice. But others believed the professor had not been strict enough, and he sided with them. "I am inexcusable for not reducing my food to the smallest quantity & simplest quality that will possibly sustain the system," his diary notes. "Oh what a slave to appetite I still am!"[37] (Was there a sexual side to his guilt? It is interesting to note that Orra would bear two more children, Charles in 1836, and Emily in 1838, when she was forty-two years old.)

After that terrible winter, Hitchcock made a full recovery. He confessed that he had begun eating more — mainly bread, butter, and milk — and the "consequence has been a greater fullness of muscle than I have had for many years."[38] He would need every ounce of strength for his next battle: convincing the world's leading scientists that his bird theory was right.

✥ THE BRITISH CONQUEST ✥

From the start, Hitchcock faced an uphill battle, finding detractors on both sides of the Atlantic. In England most scientists viewed his bird footprint idea with "the greatest skepticism,"[39] doubting that a bird could have grown so enormous. In New York geologists believed the impressions had been left by seaweed. But Hitchcock was tenacious. In the 1840s he launched a campaign to convince the world, particularly the British, that he was right. This took real nerve. Amherst was basically a backwater, and America still lacked a serious scientific tradition. Moreover, the entire country had an inferiority complex toward the British. And to make matters worse, Hitchcock did not even have a college degree.

He went, nonetheless, straight to the top. He corresponded with Charles Darwin, Gideon Mantell, Charles Lyell, and Richard Owen.[40] Initially, Owen was Hitchcock's toughest adversary. As mentioned above, he had in 1842 named the order *Dinosauria*, from which the word *dinosaur* was coined. With his distinguished lectureship in London, Owen was regarded as the world's leading comparative anatomist, an expert on the differences and similarities in animals, including fossil remains. On the question of footprints, Hitchcock considered him "better qualified to judge…than any one in Europe."[41]

Owen ruled against the professor's bird theory on two grounds: the enormous size of the tracks, and the improbability that such advanced animals could have existed so early.[42] Although Hitchcock refused to abandon his bird theory in the face of Owen's disapproval, he "trembled for it."[43]

And yet, Hitchcock had his champions, the most eminent being Charles Lyell. Lyell was the author of *Principles of Geology*, which Stephen Jay Gould called "perhaps the most important scientific textbook ever written."[44] In the 1830s, Darwin took Lyell's book with him on the *Beagle* expedition, where it proved critical to his emerging understanding of evolution. Lyell also wrote lighter fare. After touring this country in the 1840s, he published *Travels in North America; With Geological Observations on the United States, Canada, and Nova Scotia*. In 1841 he made a point of traveling to Amherst to see Hitchcock. Lyell wrote:

> April 15. Visited Professor Hitchcock at Amherst College, Massachusetts, by whom the geological survey of that State has been ably executed.... At Smith's Ferry, near Northampton, about eleven miles north of Springfield, I examined, in company with the Professor, the red sandstone on the banks of the Connecticut River, where the celebrated foot-prints of birds are beautifully exhibited.[45]

Lyell came away convinced that the fossil tracks had indeed been made by gigantic ancient birds and championed Hitchcock's views to English scientists. He noted that many naturalists had rejected the concept of an ancient bird with a foot nearly twice as large as an ostrich's. But the discovery of the moa in New Zealand, he wrote, proved the existence of "feathered bipeds" nearly as gigantic, "and reconciled the zoologist at least to the credibility of the fact, however marvellous."[46] (More on the importance of the moa in a moment.) In 1843 Lyell again defended Hitchcock's views, at a meeting of the Geological Society of London.[47] Here, Hitchcock certainly needed a champion. Although Richard Owen did not attend, he sent a note that was read aloud, stating he doubted that footprints alone were sufficient to prove whether the animals that made them were birds or reptiles.

As part of his campaign to win over the British, Hitchcock sent Darwin a copy of his hefty *Final Report on the Geology of Massachusetts*. The year was 1845. Darwin was still fifteen years away from publishing *Origin of Species*, so the professor did not find his views offensive. At the time Darwin was merely a famous naturalist, not a revolutionary. His popular reputation was based on his 1839 book, *The Voyage of the Beagle*, reporting on his round-the-world expedition. Hitchcock would also have known Darwin as a geologist, from his writings on South America and on the formation of atolls, or ring-shaped coral reefs.[48]

Darwin wrote a thank-you note from his home at Down House, southeast of London, a letter that manages to be both obsequious and damning. He was right — Darwin being right about most things — that the footprints would ensure Hitchcock's reputation. On that subject, he wrote, "your name is certain to go down to long future posterity."[49] He paid Hitchcock a great compliment, calling the footprints "one of the most curious discoveries of the present century." But he was skeptical about the bird theory, delicately implying that the track makers might have been closer to amphibians: "How sincerely I wish that you may live to discover some of the bones belonging to these gigantic birds: how eminently interesting it would be [to] know, whether their structure branches off towards the Amphibia, as I am led to imagine that you have sometime suspected."[50]

Darwin was certainly correct that fossilized bones had proved frustratingly elusive in the Connecticut Valley, for reasons I will discuss below. In his letter Darwin also mentioned that, based on a recent discovery in England, Hitchcock might still hope to find them. *Rhynchosaurus* skeletons had been found in the Grinshill Quarries of Shropshire, matching fossil footprints already known from the locality. *Rhynchosaurus*, Darwin slyly noted, was a reptile. Darwin's tone then turned humble. By nature he was shy and gentlemanly, so it is hardly surprising that he sat on his *Origin of Species* manuscript for years, loath to turn the world upside down. He ended his letter with a promise to send Hitchcock his new book, *Geological Observations on South America*, based on findings from the *Beagle* expedition. "I am preparing a little volume on the geology of South America, which, when published next summer, I wish by you to do me the privilege to accept; though it is a miserable acknowledgement for your great work. With my sincere thanks and much respect, pray believe me, dear Sir, yours faithfully & obliged, C. Darwin."

⊰ THE TRIUMPH OF THE MOA ⊱

Hitchcock's bird theory reached its apogee with the discovery of the moa. The moa was linked to a famous scientific coup. In 1839 Richard Owen theorized, based on his examination of a single six-inch section of femur, that a huge ostrich-like bird once lived in New Zealand. He would, he declared, stake his scientific reputation on the bird's existence. Three years later he received forty-seven additional moa bones that confirmed his bold prediction. Apparently the enormous flightless bird had become extinct in the not very distant past, possibly the 1700s, due to human settlement and hunting. The largest species of moa stood some sixteen feet tall, with a small head and a long, snaky neck.

If this was a coup for Owen, it was fabulous news for Hitchcock. For the first time, there was hard evidence that gigantic flightless birds had once walked the earth. Hitchcock learned of the moa in early 1843, in a letter from Lyell. Flabbergasted, he wrote back to Lyell in London, "I should as soon have thought of looking to the moon for light respecting the fossil footmarks, as to New Zealand."[51] Hitchcock made sure news of the moa promptly appeared in his usual publication, the *American Journal of Science*. Just as thrillingly, in 1844 Owen paid Hitchcock a deep compliment. In his letter he wrote, "Your beautiful discovery of the Ornithichnites ["stony bird-tracks"] has always been in my thoughts while working out the New-Zealand Bones."[52]

Even more remarkably, Owen changed his mind about Hitchcock's bird theory. Initially he had rejected it, skeptical that birds could have grown so huge or lived so long ago, but the moa discovery shifted his thinking, at least temporarily. His affirming letter to the editor of the *American Journal of Science* appeared in that publication in 1843, certainly making Hitchcock a very happy man. The moa foot bones were large enough to match the biggest Connecticut Valley footprints, Owen noted. The metatarsal — or middle — foot bone of the moa "is large enough to have sustained three toes, equivalent to produce impressions of the size of those of the *[Eubrontes] giganteus* of Prof. Hitchcock.... It seems most reasonable, therefore, to conclude that the *Ornithichnites* are the impressions of the feet of birds."[53]

By sheer good luck, Hitchcock obtained the foot bones of a moa. According to college lore, the bones came from a sailor who had died in the South Seas. His sea chest was delivered to a relative in Greenfield, Massachusetts, who discovered the bones and sent them on to Hitchcock. Hitchcock's oldest son, Edward, known as "Doc," is believed to have taken the foot to London for Richard Owen to examine. There, Doc likely carved the missing toes.

Owen further suggested that the moa might actually have been linked to the Connecticut Valley track makers. It was, he wrote, likely among the last remnants of a race of flightless birds, "which seems to have flourished at the epoch of the New Red Sandstones of Connecticut and Massachusetts."[54] Owen's letter was seen as a vindication for Hitchcock. An editor's note in the *American Journal of Science* expressed the hope that moa-like bones might be found in the Connecticut Valley to definitively prove his case. In the meantime, it stated, "let us honor the great moral courage exhibited by Hitchcock, in throwing down his opinions before an incredulous public."[55]

The British scientists apparently offered similar congratulations. According to Hitchcock, however, his endurance had a different source. As he wrote to Lyell, "I am much obliged to you, Mr. Owen, & Mr. Murchison [a Scottish geologist], for your compliment to my *moral courage* in respect to the tracks. I can only say, that the phrenologists have always given me a large organ of *obstinacy,* (I forget the name), & probably this had quite as much to do with the course I took as moral courage."[56] (In fact, the phrenologists located obstinacy at the crown of the skull, in the "organ" they called Firmness.)

Phrenological Findings

Phrenology was all the rage during Hitchcock's Amherst College presidency. This "science" was based on the idea that the shape and size of the skull revealed one's personality. The concept is complete bunk, for the brain is not a muscle, and it does not grow or shrink according to use or ability. Nonetheless, phrenologists are considered key figures in the history of cognitive psychology, for they were among the first to recognize that different parts of the brain had different functions.

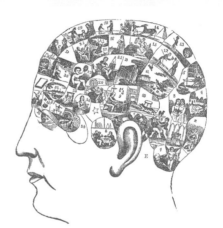

Hitchcock's skull had been analyzed by the most famous phrenologist of all, Lorenzo N. Fowler. (The little phrenology busts popular in gift shops bear his name.) In all likelihood the professor knew him personally, for Fowler attended prep school in Amherst. Hitchcock certainly knew his phrenologist brother, Orson Fowler, who graduated from Amherst College in 1834. Orson had begun his career at Amherst, performing phrenology analyses on students for two cents apiece.

Phrenology assigned a different characteristic to each part of the head, as shown in this chart. The illustration comes from Orson and Lorenzo Fowler's 1849 book The Illustrated Self-Instructor in Phrenology and Physiology, *which stated: "Most great men have great heads."*

Hitchcock refused to offer an opinion on the validity of phrenology, saying he had not adequately studied the topic.[57] Still, he appreciated the way his phrenology report confirmed his intellectual stubbornness:

> You are stable and fixed in purpose and unyielding in opinion except by the force of superior reason.... You are rather rigid as a disciplinarian yet not uncharitable — are rather conservative, but disposed to investigate all the bearings & principles of a subject in order to ferret out the truth — are liberal in opinion but tenacious of your convictions of right.[58]

To the British scientists, Hitchcock sent not only his book but a more unusual gift as well: fossilized excrement — coprolites, to use the proper term. He sent these to Gideon Mantell and possibly also to Richard Owen, judging by the thank-you notes he received.[59] Hitchcock believed the droppings came from ancient birds, not dinosaurs, and he thought he had the chemical analysis to prove it.

The word *coprolite* — from the Greek *kopros*, meaning dung — was coined in 1829 by the pioneering English geologist William Buckland, who had arrived at the discovery through discussions with fellow naturalists Mantell and Mary Anning. They had noted the presence of peculiar stones in the abdomens of fossilized marine animals called *Ichthyosaurs*. Buckland then published a paper, "On the Discovery of Coprolites, or Fossil Faeces."[60] Although certain Oxford University colleagues looked askance at his scatological pursuits, Buckland didn't care. To him, coprolites lent fossils a kind of thrilling immediacy. He wrote, "When we see the body of an *Ichthyosaurus* still containing the food it had eaten just before its death, ten thousand, or more than ten thousand times ten thousand years ago, all these vast intervals seem annihilated, come together, disappear, and we are almost brought into as immediate contact with events of immeasurably distant periods as with the affairs of yesterday."[61]

As for Hitchcock, he was hardly squeamish about the subject. He discovered coprolites in about 1844, in hard, chalky rock at Chicopee Falls, Massachusetts, where the fossil footprints were unusually dense. "In the midst of them," he wrote, "I found a few ovoid flattened bodies, about an inch in diameter, and perhaps two inches long, of a dark color, and considerably softer than the enclosing rock."[62]

Buckland had sent his coprolites for chemical analysis to William Wollaston, a fellow member of the London Geological Society. Wollaston found high concentrations of phosphate of lime, indicating that the *Ichthyosaurs* might have been carnivores, the lime being the residue of other animals' bones. (Starting in 1850, England even had a coprolite industry. Coprolites were dug out of fields near Cambridge, where they occurred in huge quantities, and used as fertilizer.)

Following Buckland's example, Hitchcock sent his samples off for chemical analysis. Samuel Dana, a skilled chemist in Lowell, Massachusetts, had the proper pedigree: in 1842 he had described the role of phosphates in fertilizer made from manure. The professor hoped that Dana would prove that the specimens were indeed fossilized excrement. Moreover, he hoped that Dana would detect the presence of uric acid, which he believed would indicate that the droppings came from birds. Unlike mammals, which excrete urea, birds excrete uric acid, which is relatively nontoxic, and so does not poison embryos inside of eggs.

Dana came through. The substance was indeed a coprolite, "the excrement of an animal dropped perhaps hundreds of thousands of years ago."[63] Even better, he isolated half a percent of uric acid in the ancient droppings. This led him, wrote Hitchcock, "to infer, by fair reasoning, that it is the coprolite of birds, rather than of any other animal."[64] Reptiles, he argued, would have excreted a higher percentage of uric acid, in the form of pure urine. Further, he observed, the coprolite appeared to come not from a carnivorous bird but from an omnivore. Both Hitchcock and Dana noted the presence of something highly interesting in the coprolites: small black grains. Working independently, they arrived at the same conclusion. As Dana stated in his paper, "Now allow me a word of speculation. I cannot but think these black grains are *seeds*, which have passed undigested through the intestines."[65] Undigested seeds, he argued, are typically found in bird excrement.

Hitchcock used coprolites — fossilized excrement — to bolster his theory that the local tracks had been made by gigantic ancient birds. These coprolites are from the college's collection.

So thrilled was Hitchcock about the results that he could not resist a Christian metaphor. "Truly," he wrote, "this may be called a scientific miracle — a resurrection from the dead, and among the many analogous miracles wrought in the nineteenth century I know of scarcely any more marvellous than this!"[66] From excrement came vivid evidence of ancient life.

Owen, in London, seemed impressed. Hitchcock had sent him the papers discussing the coprolite analysis, perhaps accompanied by actual specimens. He responded in 1844, "Prof. Dana's skilful analysis has yielded a beautiful and most unexpected corroboration of the accuracy of your original deductions of the class of animals to which the footprints belonged."[67] He also, however, pointed to a flaw in the argument. He refused to rule out the possibility that the coprolites came from reptiles: "We must bear in mind, however, that in all the Ovipara, with the cloaca, the urine blends with the excrement."[68] (Ovipara means egg layers — reptiles as well as birds.) Nonetheless, Hitchcock felt that his bird thesis had been upheld.

Even as he was stubbornly making his bird case to the English, Hitchcock had other projects in the works. Most important, he wrote his textbook, *Elementary Geology*, first published in1840. It ranked among the earliest authentically American geology textbooks, not merely adapted from the British. A great success, the book was popular in colleges across the country, going through thirty-one editions during Hitchcock's lifetime.

Geology was still a young field. As Hitchcock wrote in the lecture notes for his geology class, "no science has within a few years made more rapid progress than this. It is in fact one of the latest of the sciences, and although many a wild theory of the earth was with much travail ushered into the world a century ago, yet legitimate geology cannot claim an age of half this duration."[69]

Still, even "legitimate geology" had one foot in the Bible. In the 1830s scientists were hotly debating the effects of Noah's flood. Hitchcock had his own ideas on the subject, and it is fascinating to trace his thinking over several decades. Initially he found evidence of the biblical deluge right here in Massachusetts. In his 1832 geologic map of the state, the professor identified a formation he called Diluvium, which covered Plymouth and most of Cape Cod with a surface of gravel, loam, sand, and boulders. Diluvium was a direct reference to the biblical deluge, Noah's flood. In fact, Hitchcock was seeing evidence of the last Ice Age.

In his 1833 report on the state's geology, he noted that Massachusetts *"has been modified by a powerful deluge, sweeping from the north and northwest, over every part of the State; not excepting its highest mountains."*[70] (Italics his.) This vast flood also explained the presence of huge, isolated rocks on flat surfaces, rocks that scientists now call erratic boulders. Hitchcock maintained that the flood also accounted for the long scratches and grooves found in rocks statewide. In short, he argued, scientists could not rule out the notion that Noah's flood had swept over Massachusetts.

Yet Hitchcock was not immune to the scientific shifts of the 1830s. In this case, he actually changed his mind — though he would still be wrong. First, Lyell's *Principles of Geology* began to make intellectual inroads, convincing geologists that the biblical deluge had not occurred worldwide. Then, a second revolutionary idea came to the fore. In 1837 the eminent Swiss-born naturalist Louis Agassiz began disseminating the concept of a great Ice Age.[71] At first, few believed that glaciers had once buried much of the Northern Hemisphere under thousands of feet of ice, but gradually, most geologists came to embrace Agassiz's view. Hitchcock never did accept the concept of the Ice Age. Instead, he traded his Noah's flood idea for a vision involving icebergs.

By 1840 he had abandoned the idea that the biblical flood had created the rock formations on Cape Cod. The gravel layer he had called Diluvium was rechristened "drift." When Lyell visited Hitchcock in 1841, drift was a major topic of conversation. Discussing how moraines — mounds of drift — might have been formed in Massachusetts, both rejected the idea that they had been left by glaciers, attributing them instead "to the melting of icebergs charged with fragments of gravel and rock."[72]

Hitchcock rejected the Ice Age idea partly because he was skeptical that the earth's climate could have undergone such dramatic and rapid change. He knew that the Connecticut Valley climate had once been nearly tropical, judging from the fossilized plants found alongside the footprints.[73] And thus he found it "difficult to imagine a cause for a sudden change on the earth's surface from almost tropical to an ultra-arctic climate, without supposing a total change in the present arrangements of the solar system."[74] Instead, he believed in the power of both ice and water— icebergs. What we now call glacial moraines, he called iceberg moraines. Under this scenario, continents rose up, mountains sent down glaciers, and then huge chunks of ice broke off, loaded with debris. When these icebergs melted, they left behind erratic boulders as well as drift.[75]

Ironically, Hitchcock's name has been immortalized on geologic maps for a phenomenon of the Ice Age. Glacial Lake Hitchcock, named in his

Hitchcock made this astronomical instrument while principal of Deerfield Academy (1816 to 1819) for the purpose of calculating eclipses. During this time he acquired a measure of fame for his astronomical prowess. Edmund Blunt, publisher of a nautical almanac, had promised $10 to anyone who caught an error. When Hitchcock submitted a list of fifty-seven mistakes, the publisher refused to pay up. Outraged, Hitchcock sent an account of this deceit to American Monthly Magazine, *and Blunt was publicly embarrassed.*

honor, is the vast body of water that filled the Connecticut River valley some 15,000 years ago. (At that time, the Amherst College hill formed an island in the lake.) Glacial Lake Hitchcock was held in place for some 3,000 years by a rock dam at Rocky Hill, Connecticut. Eventually erosion breached it, and the water poured down to the sea, marking the birth of the Connecticut River. Although

Hitchcock did not detect the lake, he laid the groundwork for its discovery. In 1857 he had published an admirably detailed study of the contours of the Connecticut Valley titled *Illustrations of Surface Geology.*[76]

As for Cape Cod, modern scientists have determined that it was not formed by Noah's flood. Its gravelly surface was deposited by a melting glacier at the end of the last Ice Age. The land was formed when the glacier retreated some 18,000 years ago, leaving behind the familiar sheltering arm.

✦ A FEMINIST ✦

Hitchcock's gravestone describes him as "a lover of men." He was also a lover of women, in the best sense, believing that women deserved a rigorous education. In an era when most men considered women constitutionally unfit for higher learning, and many feared that knowledge would tarnish their virtue, Hitchcock maintained that the study of natural history brought people closer to God, and that women would be elevated by that pursuit.

And so, he taught science to girls and women. He shaped the education of none other than Emily Dickinson, whose poetry is peppered with technical and scientific terms. He also instructed Mary Lyon, founder of Mount Holyoke College (then Female Seminary), among the country's first institutions of higher learning for women. For more than thirty years, he was her friend and backer, even writing her biography after she died. (Were they in love? I doubt it; they were both too busy. She devoted herself to teaching and never married.)

In 1835 Mary Lyon lived with the Hitchcocks in their Amherst home, sleeping in "the upper back room."[77] The professor taught her natural science, with an emphasis on her specialty of chemistry, while Orra Hitchcock taught her scientific illustration. It was during this time that Lyon formulated her plans for founding Mount Holyoke. Hitchcock, although instrumental in communicating those plans to the public, made one unfortunate blunder. In his scholarly zeal, he proposed that the school take a pretentious Greek name, *Pangynaskean.* Newspaper editors gleefully lampooned the "whole-woman-making school."[78] Despite this setback, Lyon managed to obtain the funding for her seminary, whose doors opened in 1837. Her curriculum required seven courses in mathematics and science for graduation, something unheard-of at other women's seminaries. She introduced women to the idea of performing their own laboratory experiments, and she organized field trips, taking students to collect plants and minerals, view geologic formations, and, yes, see Hitchcock's fossil footprints.

At her death in 1849, Hitchcock wrote a heartfelt tribute, "A Chapter in the

Autumn Scenery, *an Amherst view by Orra White Hitchcock.*

Book of Providence," that was later expanded into a full-length biography, *The Life and Labors of Mary Lyon.* In part he drew on descriptions from her colleagues and friends. But, he noted, "I may be allowed to add that it is no second-hand representation which I make, but one founded upon a personal and intimate acquaintance of more than thirty years, during which my house was frequently made her home."[79] The professor had tremendous admiration for her drive, her seriousness, and — in contrast to him — her nerves of steel. A devout Christian, Lyon was also a strict teacher with little patience for the niceties of fashionable life. She relegated to the lowest priority such typical women's subjects as music, painting, and embroidery. Some detractors, he admitted, found her too stern and complained that "many of the minor graces and elegant accomplishments, which give a charm to female loveliness, were too much neglected."[80] If she erred on the side of strictness, this was because she had grown disgusted with all that was impractical and superficial in women's education.

It was during Lyon's last full year of teaching, in 1847, that Emily Dickinson came to Mount Holyoke. Dickinson had grown up under Hitchcock's intellectual shadow, exposed to some of the most sophisticated scientific ideas in the country. The professor had influenced the curriculum at Amherst Academy, where the town's elite students, including Dickinson, were schooled. Dickinson then attended Mount Holyoke for one year, where she would have studied botany, geology, and chemistry. A letter written to her brother, Austin, read, "Your welcome letter found me all engrossed in the history of Sulphuric Acid!!!!!"[81] Her technical acumen found its way into her poems: some 270 contain scientific terms, including "phosphor," "species," "entomology," "pyrite," "corolla," and "atom."[82] Yet Dickinson ultimately rejected Hitchcock's potent blend of science and evangelical Christianity. At Mount Holyoke she famously attended a schoolwide revival meeting led by Mary Lyon. When Lyon asked all those who wanted to be Christians to stand, Dickinson alone remained seated.

The professor may also have influenced Dickinson's use of language. Although he was a scientist, "there was a touch of the poet in everything he did,"[83] noted Richard Sewall, in his Dickinson biography. Cited as particularly inspirational to her is one of my favorite books by Hitchcock, *Religious Lectures on Peculiar Phenomena in the Four Seasons.* This charming little volume first appeared in 1849, when Dickinson was eighteen years old. According to inventories of the family library, the Dickinsons owned a copy. The book is transporting. Hitchcock devotes one lecture to each season, focusing on natural occurrences that to him had religious significance. With spring comes resurrection, as hibernating animals awaken and butterflies emerge from their cocoons. Summer brings the rainbow, sign of God's covenant. Autumn brings a kind of glorious death, and winter the diamond radiance of an ice storm, revealing the splendor of God's works. This valley, where Hitchcock once lived and I still do, is famed for its autumn foliage, but who would dare describe it? One risks cliché or simply bad taste. But the professor did justice to the leaves:

> Red of every shade, from crimson to cherry, — yellow from bright sulphur to orange, — brown, from clove-brown to liver-brown, — and green, from grassgreen to oil-green, — stand forth in distinct spots, yet all mingled in fantastic proportions, and clothing the landscape with an almost dazzling brilliancy; especially when lighted up by the mellow rays of an October sun.[84]

One of Dickinson's later poems may pay homage to Hitchcock. Sewall suggests that in "The Lilac is an Ancient Shrub," written about 1872, he may well be "the Scientist of Faith":[85]

> …The Scientist of Faith
> His research has but just begun —
> Above his Synthesis
> The Flora unimpeachable
> To Time's Analysis —
>
> "Eye hath not seen" may possibly
> Be current with the Blind

But let not Revelation
By Theses be detained —

And yet it is not the scientist whose works have withstood time's analysis. Every one of Hitchcock's books remains out of print. Dickinson, adopting a more secular voice, emerged as the genius who transcended her era.

⊰ THE CREATIONIST ⊱

Dickinson's poetry would hardly have pleased Hitchcock, judging from his 1845 inaugural address as Amherst College president. He had little tolerance for literature unless it was of the strictly Christian kind. Poetry, he stated, "is the appropriate language of all strong emotions; and may, therefore, be employed for giving an attractive dress to immoral and irreligious sentiments."[86]

In that long and fascinating address, Hitchcock also laid out his views on evolution — or, as he called it, "the transmutation of species."[87] More than a decade before Darwin published his *Origin of Species*, evolution was already raising the hackles of natural theologians, who believed that God could be found in the study of nature. (Darwin is often considered the originator of evolutionary theory, but this is incorrect. Darwin's true breakthrough lay in discovering the mechanism of natural selection.) Before Darwin, the foremost advocate of evolution was the French biologist Jean-Baptiste Lamarck. As evidenced in his 1847 textbook, Hitchcock disagreed with him. For Hitchcock and other theologians of his era, the idea that humans had evolved from apes was particularly galling. He cited with scorn Lamarck's idea that the human race began as a mere *monad*, or particle, "and was converted into several animals successively; the ourang-outan being his last condition, before he became man."[88]

Contrary to Lamarck, Hitchcock embraced the notion that has so oddly made a comeback in recent years: intelligent design. Under this rubric, nothing was random. There was no place for a cruel, mechanistic device like survival of the fittest. Hitchcock believed that God had created (and destroyed) successive generations of animals, in separate acts of creation. Each species was designed to perfectly fit the niche in which it lived. (This is a lovely idea, but it has no basis in science, and it explains nothing at all about the reality of the natural world. By contrast, evolution explains all kinds of phenomena, from the gradual lengthening of hummingbird beaks over time to drug resistance in bacteria.)

Lamarck believed that species had evolved from the simple to the complex. Hitchcock did recognize the general trend of increasing complexity in the fossil record, as one moved up through the rock layers.[89] Yet he also sought exceptions to this rule — for otherwise he risked supporting the notion that human beings had evolved from lower life forms. For his examples, he looked to fossil fish, citing species that showed a "retrograde" tendency over time, with complex fish later being replaced by simpler forms.[90]

Taking another swipe at evolution, Hitchcock noted that fossil fish changed dramatically from one geologic period to the next. Devonian fish had nothing in common with Jurassic ones, he stated. Moreover, some Jurassic fish had no counterpart among modern species. To Hitchcock, these sudden shifts showed that species did not undergo gradual transformations through a natural process. "Here, on the contrary," he wrote, "we find such great and entire changes in the successive groups as can be explained only by new creations."[91] In this, he sided with Harvard's Louis Agassiz, who clung to his creationist beliefs to his dying day, in 1873. Agassiz held that the making of every species resided "in the thought of the Creator."[92]

As for the Amherst College presidency, Hitchcock donned that mantle only with great reluctance. One can hardly blame him, given that the college was teetering on the verge of bankruptcy. His efforts to revive the institution brought astonishingly rapid results. In 1847, just two years into his term, his diary exults, "Well, another Collegiate year has past and *what a year!*"[93] The good news was that philanthropist Samuel Williston of Easthampton had donated $30,000. That sum, plus additional donations totaling $74,000, meant that the college could pay off its debts and endow three professorships. Hitchcock had saved the institution. "The tone of public sentiment also is entirely changed," he noted, "& the general feeling is that now Amherst college must live & flourish, & it was delightful at Commencement to see so many happy faces of alumni & friends."[94]

Hitchcock discovered this plant, the small grape fern (Botrychium simplex), and named it for science in 1823. Sadly, most of his early botanical collection was destroyed by worms. About thirty plant specimens he collected can be found at the herbarium of the University of Massachusetts, Amherst. Courtesy of Archives and Special Collections, Amherst College Library.

Williston, the benefactor, was not even an Amherst graduate. Weak eyesight had kept him out of college altogether. A manufacturer of buttons and elastic, he established Easthampton Rubber Thread Company not far from Amherst — and made a fortune. Over the course of his lifetime he would give what was then an enormous sum to Amherst College, some $220,000. In return for his generosity, Amherst seriously considered changing its name to Williston College. The trustees balked, a fact that did not sit well with the professor, who felt that Williston deserved the honor. Hitchcock remained president of the college until 1854, despite his complaints about the crushing responsibilities of his position. Never did he have fewer than forty unanswered letters on his desk, awaiting reply.[95] Yet he was heartened during his term by several religious revivals at the college.

After stepping down from the presidency, he was able to return full time to his studies of fossil footprints, in 1858 publishing his magnum opus, *Ichnology of New England*. If that year brought triumph, the next brought the opposite. Darwin's *Origin of Species*, published in 1859, would topple Hitchcock's entire worldview. God had no place in natural selection, and Darwin's case for evolution proved so overwhelming that, within a decade, virtually all serious scientists were convinced.[96]

Perhaps, it was fortunate that Hitchcock did not live long enough to see that intellectual revolution take place. The thirty-first and final edition of his geology textbook appeared in 1863, just a year before his death. Hitchcock warned his readers not to be swayed by those scientists who advocated evolution, "with Darwin at their head."[97] While the book dismisses Darwin, it appeared early enough in the debate so as not to seem ridiculous.

In fact, evolution remained a controversial topic at Amherst College until the twentieth century. In 1877 President Julius Seelye effectively banned the teaching of Darwin's theories on campus. The college's biology department went along with his directive, instructing students in what would today be called creationism. (Benjamin Kendall Emerson, professor of geology and zoology, defied Seelye, and insisted on teaching evolution anyway.)

❧ THE RELIGION OF GEOLOGY ❧

Before returning to the all-important footprints, let us take a brief detour into Hitchcock's intellectual life. He called himself a professor of "natural theology" — as opposed to natural history — and he took that title seriously. As Francis Bacon defined it, natural theology was "that spark of knowledge of God which may be had by the light of nature and the consideration of created things."[98]

Scholars often argue that the scientific revolution would not have been possible without the Protestant Reformation, which replaced Catholic mysticism with a more rationalist view.[99] Protestant scholars like Hitchcock looked for proof of God not in ritual, but in physical evidence of the natural world. They also took very seriously the words of the Bible, an approach that led to increasing theological difficulties in the nineteenth century, as scientific advances began to strain the credibility of biblical accounts of the natural world.[100] Catholics, by contrast, found the scientific revolution less troubling, because they had never looked for God in nature. As one scholar put it, Cardinal Newman "did not rely on astronomy to sustain the faith."[101]

Hitchcock and other natural theologians felt a deep reverence for the Bible, yet — despite the way they are often portrayed — they did not take it literally. The professor gently ridiculed those who, at the dawn of the Renaissance, dismissed the Copernican view of the solar system because it contradicted the biblical view that the sun revolved around the earth.[102] At the same time, however, Hitchcock was unwilling to dismiss the Bible as *irrelevant* to a scientific view of the world. In order to reconcile the Bible and the natural world, he and his fellow natural theologians were forced to interpret scripture more and more figuratively. It was an endeavor that required marvelous creativity, as the following examples reveal.

In Hitchcock's era the historical reality of Noah's ark was a topic of heated debate. Here was the problem: the ark was becoming terribly overcrowded. By the 1850s biologists had identified some 150,000 distinct species of animals. Christian ministers were hard-pressed to explain how 300,000 animals (each species with its mate) could have squeezed onto the ark. In his 1851 book *The Religion of Geology*, Hitchcock admitted this would have been impossible. But he devised a clever twist to make the biblical account plausible,[103] suggesting that the flood had covered only the Middle East, a region with relatively few animal species. This smaller subset of creatures, he argued, could have comfortably fit on board.

He also grappled with the ancient age of the earth. He knew that the planet was far more than 6,000 years old, the age calculated by theologians based on the Bible. Charles Lyell's influential *Principles of Geology*, published in 1830, convincingly argued that the earth's crust had been formed by natural events taking place over millions of years, not by Noah's flood or other occurrences noted in the Bible. Hitchcock knew from his own observations of rock layers that the Connecticut Valley was vastly more than 6,000 years old. At one point, he mentioned that his fossil footprints might date back "hundreds of thousands" of years.[104]

Still, he refused to dismiss the Bible's validity. To bring Genesis into line with geology, he looked closely at biblical language, going back to the original Hebrew to make his point.[105] He examined the opening lines: "In the beginning God created the heavens and the earth. And the earth was desolate...." Hitchcock zeroed in on the word "And" that begins the second sentence. He pointed out that "and" is a translation of the Hebrew "v'," which arguably has more than one meaning. He noted that "v'" can also mean "afterwards." This allowed Hitchcock to read Genesis in a dramatically different way: In the beginning God created the heavens and the earth. *Afterwards* — meaning over vast spans of geologic time — the earth was desolate, while it was being formed. Voilà.

With a bit of imaginative interpretation, Genesis agreed with geology.[106]

Hitchcock was squarely a man of his time. What distinguishes him, beyond his many achievements, may be that he tried harder than any other American scientist of his era to bridge the realms of science and religion. In 1859 he published a second edition of *The Religion of Geology*. His preface responded to the storm of criticism he had received from both sides — Christian believers as well as scientific unbelievers — following publication of the first edition. Seemingly he had made peace with himself. He wrote:

> The Infidel raves furiously, because I have endeavored to make Geology sustain and illustrate revelation; but my Christian friend declares my book to be thoroughly infidel. One of the parties must surely be mistaken in its bearing. Till they can settle that question, I think I may rest quietly. Like an acid and an alkali in chemistry, the two attacks neutralize each other, and leave me unharmed.[107]

✢ BIRDS WITH FOUR LEGS ✦

While the controversy raged over his attempts to reconcile religion and science, Hitchcock continued to pursue his paleontology. In 1858, at the age of sixty-five, he published his great scientific work, *Ichnology of New England*, recording his observations on the fossil footprints in exhaustive detail. He continued to insist that the "footmarks," as he called them, had been made by birds. Just what did these ancient birds look like, in his mind's eye? If ever he attempted an illustration, I have not found it. There exists one passage, however, containing a vivid description of his strange menagerie. He imagined, walking about in the mud, a flock of apterous (flightless) birds some twelve feet tall. With them was a gigantic biped — "a bird, perhaps":

> I have experienced all the excitement of romance, as I have gone back into those immensely remote ages, and watched those shores along which these enormous and heteroclitic beings walked. Now I have seen, in scientific vision, an apterous bird, some twelve or fifteen feet high, — nay, large flocks of them, — walking over the muddy surface, followed by many others of analogous character, but of smaller size. Next comes a biped animal, a bird, perhaps, with a foot and heel nearly two feet long. Then a host of lesser bipeds, formed on the same general type.[108]

Sadly for Hitchcock, by the time *Ichnology of New England* appeared, in 1858, his bird theory was being eclipsed. Fossil finds in Europe had allowed the study of dinosaur anatomy to grow vastly more sophisticated. Indeed, scientists were starting to understand that the entire Mesozoic era — through the Triassic, Jurassic,

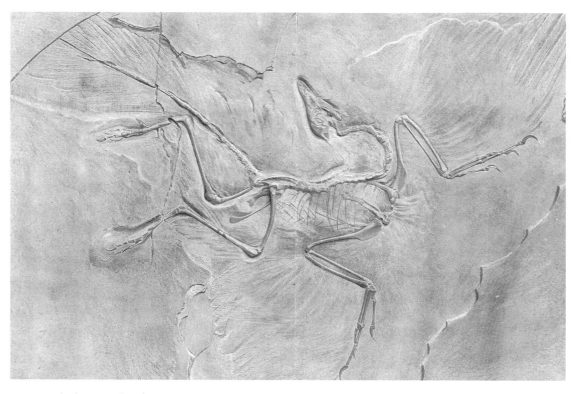

The discovery of Archeopteryx *in 1861 should have derailed Hitchcock's bird theory. Instead, he tried to use it to his advantage.*

and Cretaceous periods — was dominated by dinosaurs. The very year his *Ichnology* was published, Hitchcock's bird thesis faced an even greater challenge: the first major dinosaur find in the United States. A *Hadrosaurus* skeleton was discovered in New Jersey and described by the pioneering American paleontologist Joseph Leidy. Based on its sturdy back legs and small front appendages, Leidy concluded that the animal walked on two legs. It certainly did not resemble a bird. Hitchcock mentioned the "remarkable reptile" in his 1863 textbook, describing the *Hadrosaurus* as "a huge herbivorous saurian, closely allied to the *Iguanodon*, probably twenty-five feet long, whose thigh bone is nearly a third longer than that of a common mastodon. Its tail was three feet deep."[109] No footprints were found with the skeleton.

In 1859 Hitchcock received a shot across the bow. Roswell Field, an amateur fossil hunter, declared that the Connecticut Valley footprints had been made not by birds but by reptiles. Field made a pointed speech right in Hitchcock's backyard, at a meeting of the American Association for the Advancement of Science in Springfield, Massachusetts. Although he was not a scientist, Field had undeniable expertise. He owned the farm where thousands of fossil tracks had been quarried, up the river in the town of Gill. Over the years Field had examined countless footprints and drawn his own conclusions about the animals that made them. "If I have not studied this subject in vain they were all quadrupedal,"[110] he wrote in an 1860 article in the *American Journal of Science*. "That they usually walked on two feet I admit, and that they could as readily walk on four when necessary is equally true." And, he continued, "it is plain that they dragged their tails in the mud, leaving a groove plowed up from one-half inch to an inch in width." Such tail marks, he observed, appeared only when the animal's feet had sunk deep in the mud. (On all these points Field turned out to be absolutely right.)

Field went on to dismiss the eminent Hitchcock's views. Then, with unmistakable condescension, he offered an excuse for the professor's error: "I would only add that when fossil tracks were first discovered there was so little known of the formation of the feet of fossil or of living animals, and particularly of their footprints, that it is possible the first discoverers might have been mistaken as to the ornithic character of the footprints."[111]

It must have pained Hitchcock that Field's remarks were taken seriously and moreover published in the journal to which Hitchcock regularly submitted his own work. He felt so unnerved that in 1861 he sent a searching letter to Owen in London. In it, he explained that certain writers had disputed the idea that the fossil footprints had been made by birds. Noting certain puzzling characteristics of the footprints, he asked Owen: If the track makers weren't birds, what were they? Does any existing animal show such characteristics of the feet? The reply, if any, has not survived. Owen did, however, comment on an exciting specimen brought to him in London by Hitchcock's son, to which I will return below.

In 1861 came a damaging discovery, one that should have left the professor deeply discouraged. A beautifully preserved skeleton of *Archaeopteryx* had been found in the famous limestone fossil beds of

A few local fossil bones were found at last in 1860, four years before Hitchcock's death. At the time, opinions were inconclusive regarding whether the bones belonged to a dinosaur or a more birdlike creature. Later the species — a dinosaur after all — was named Anchisaurus. *This specimen reveals the bones of a hand.*

Solnhofen, Germany. The feathered specimen, clearly a transitional form between reptile and bird, was known to be from the late Jurassic period. Hitchcock believed his Connecticut Valley footprints to be from a much earlier time, either the late Triassic or the early Jurassic. Here was the damning question: If *Archaeopteryx* looked so primitive, then how could the much earlier Connecticut Valley track makers have been more sophisticated ostrichlike birds? (It is worth noting that Victorian-era scientists had no way to date rock formations or the age of the earth. Instead, they organized fossils according to rock layers, with the oldest at the bottom. Hitchcock knew that his sandstone footprints would have been separated from *Archaeopteryx* by thousands of feet of rock, with *Archaeopteryx* far higher up.)[112]

Hitchcock was not to be deterred. In his last book, *Supplement to the Ichnology of New England*, he stubbornly used *Archaeopteryx* to support his bird theory "with more confidence than ever."[113] He found remarkable resemblances between the "feathered fossil" of Solnhofen and certain of his fossil footprints. *Archaeopteryx* was a quadruped, with small front feet. Hitchcock also had good footprints from a quadruped, which he named *Anomoepus*. He noted that in both *Archaeopteryx* and *Anomoepus*, the hind feet had three front toes, and the same number of phalanges, or toe bones. The foot of a reptile, he argued, would not have had the same number of phalanges.

A bird with four legs? Clearly, by the time Hitchcock wrote his *Supplement* (published the year after he died), his view of what constituted a bird was becoming more complex. In the case of a bird with four feet, he wrote, "I have imagined that in such a case the anterior feet would be very peculiar, and not ordinarily used for locomotion."[114] Certainly, this perfectly describes the strange little arms of many dinosaur species.

If a bird could have four legs, could it not also have a tail? *Archaeopteryx* had a tail, about six inches long. Hitchcock noted that his *Anomoepus* must also have had a tail, which, "although rarely leaving an impression, did sometimes drag along and make a narrow continuous trail."[115] He then made a new discovery. Although he had long pored over the footprints, he sometimes noticed new features. On one slab he found grooves "as if some flipper-like appendage had dragged behind the animal."[116] These marks suggested "the idea of a broad and singular tail."[117]

So now he had two types of ancient track makers. One group consisted of birds with four legs and a tail; the other more closely resembled modern birds. Hitchcock argued that four-footed animals like *Archaeopteryx* and *Anomoepus* belonged to a "lower," more primitive group of birds. He believed these lower birds lived alongside the more "perfect" birds that had made most of his fossil tracks. He admitted that ancient birds "may have exhibited forms very different from the perfect bird-type of the present day."[118] Yet fundamentally, he wrote, "I see no characters in their tracks that ally them to any other animals."[119] Finally, after examining all the facts, he asked, "How then could I avoid the conclusion that these animals were birds? Doubtless with some peculiarities of structure… but still decidedly birds."[120] In truth, Hitchcock's vision of the track makers was quite close to the way scientists have imagined the Connecticut Valley dinosaurs. If only he could have relinquished the word *bird*!

In the meantime, Hitchcock was corresponding with Yale's James Dwight Dana, associate editor of the *American Journal of Science*. Dana presciently argued that some ancient animals had characteristics of both birds and reptiles. "The world," he declared, "will have finally to settle down to the belief that there were Reptilian Birds in ancient times."[121] Although this view differed slightly from his own, Hitchcock liked Dana's remarks enough to include them in his *Supplement to the Ichnology of New England*.

Hitchcock compared his fossil footprints to the tracks of many modern animals — even salamanders, as this illustration shows.

Would bones solve the mystery? Not entirely. For decades the whole paleontological world had been hoping that fossil bones might be found, to shed some light on the ancient Connecticut Valley track makers. Finally, in 1860, part of a skeleton was unearthed. William Smith, while overseeing some blasting work in Springfield, found a hand, four vertebrae, part of a femur, and part of an ischia, or wishbone. Smith presented the bones to Hitchcock, who in turn took them to the distinguished Harvard anatomist Jeffries Wyman. Wyman failed to resolve the dilemma. His first conclusion about the bones was that "There can be no question that they are those of a reptile."[122] But then he noted that the most remarkable feature of the bones was that they were hollow — and he admitted that this feature "might be referred to birds."[123]

Hitchcock's elder son, Edward (known as "Doc") took the bones to Richard Owen in London. Owen opined that they belonged to a "Saurian Reptile" — a dinosaur. Yet he too left open the possibility that the hollow bones, if filled with oil or light marrow, would "point to a course of development toward

Pterodactyles or Birds."[124] Owen placed the animal in a new genus, *Megadactylus*, named for the large dactyl bone in its foot. Doc Hitchcock added the species name *polyzelus*, meaning "much sought after," alluding to the long search in the Connecticut Valley for fossil bones.

Time was running out for Hitchcock's bird theory. In late 1867 the famous dinosaur hunter Edward Drinker Cope addressed the Academy of Natural Sciences in Philadelphia, arguing that even the most birdlike tracks of the Connecticut Valley had been made by dinosaurs.[125] Then, in 1885, Othniel Marsh, Cope's rival in the dinosaur "bone wars," reclassified the *Megadactylus* skeleton. He removed it from its old footprint genus and placed it in a proper dinosaur genus, *Anchisaurus*. The species name, *polyzelus*, he retained. But even a dinosaur skeleton did not solve the mystery of the Connecticut Valley footprints: ironically, the hand of the *Anchisaurus* does not quite fit any of Hitchcock's tracks.

❧ DEATH ❧

As the professor approached the age of seventy, he began thinking not only about the world to come, but also about his legacy to Amherst College. What he concluded does not show him in his best light, for it reveals a certain narrow-mindedness. In 1860 Hitchcock worried about the possibility of "religious error" at the college. He was concerned that the school might eventually fall into the hands of "such men as it was founded to counteract & defeat — say Unitarians, Universalists & Infidels." He stopped short of amending his will, knowing that such legal injunctions were rarely followed. Instead, he spelled out in his diary, for his heirs to read, exactly what he wanted done with his fossil footprints if the college were no longer led by evangelical Christians with beliefs similar to his own. "Should the College pass in to the hands of men who reject this system, I want them to feel that they have no right to use my collections but should give them up to my heirs."[126] The only acceptable Christian denominations besides his own were Baptist, Presbyterian, Methodist, and Episcopalian — and only to members of these churches would he extend "the right hand of fellowship."[127] He admitted that some might see his view as bigoted. "I leave every man at liberty to adopt what creed in religion he pleases," he wrote. "But if he adopt another Gospel I do not wish to aid him in promoting it. If this is bigotry, be it so. It is what seems to me to be right in the near view of death."[128] By the early twentieth century Amherst College had become a mainly secular institution, yet Hitchcock's heirs chose not to follow his wishes. His fabulous track collections remain at the college.[129]

Workaholic that he was, Hitchcock hardly seemed to slow down in his final years. He had lived so long with the idea that he was on the brink of death — since his late teens — that perhaps the final chapter was anticlimactic. One of his most remarkable accomplishments came in 1862, at the age of sixty-seven. Having complained in his diary of a wracking cough, bleeding lungs, diabetes, muscle weakness, the usual dyspepsia and "an indescribable feeling of universal failure of the powers of life,"[130] he sat down and wrote a four-hundred-page manuscript in just six months. The book was *Reminiscences of Amherst College.*

The following year he lost his dear wife, Orra, whose health had been declining for some time. In 1855 she had fallen off her porch, an accident from which she never completely recovered. A few years later her eyes began to fail and her hands grew shaky.[131] At the time of her death, the professor was too ill even to pick up a pen, but asked someone, perhaps a daughter, to notate:

> June 6, 1863. God has spared me to make one more entry in this journal, by an amanuensis. The most unexpected and perhaps the most important of all which it contains. It is the death of my beloved wife, who left us Tuesday, May 26th at 6 o'clock p.m. and so quietly and without suffering did she pass away, that it made death rather attractive than repulsive to us all. O, if we could only go as she did, who would not be willing to make the exchange of worlds. And now Lord, what remains for me, but to go?[132]

Emily Dickinson, then thirty-three, wryly recorded a moment from Orra's funeral service, in a letter to her cousins Louise and Frances Norcross:

> Jennie Hitchcock's mother was buried yesterday, so there is one orphan more, and her father is very sick besides. My father and mother went to the service, and mother said while the minister prayed, a hen with her chickens came up, and tried to fly into the window. I suppose the dead lady used to feed them, and they wanted to bid her good-by. Life is death we're lengthy at, death the hinge to life.[133]

Hitchcock cherished the hope that he would meet his wife in heaven. He himself was indeed very sick, yet he held on for another nine months, surviving most of the winter. On January 4 he wrote another diary entry:

> Oh marvellous! That I should be alive to make this record in the year 1864. It is not so easy to see why the silver thread is not yet broken, but God I trust will show me why & what I have to do. To do? Surely it must be an infinitessimal labour. But great or small let it be for God's glory & my last my best work.[134]

There is a final, incomplete entry a few days later, part of it missing, or perhaps removed by the family in the interest of privacy. He died on February 27. As Richard Sewall wrote in his Dickinson biography, "When Edward Hitchcock died in 1864, Amherst knew it had lost a great man."[135]

His tombstone stands in Amherst's West Cemetery, a white obelisk not far from Emily Dickinson's grave. His inscription calls him:

A Leader in Science
A Lover of Men
A Friend of God

The obelisk does not mention Hitchcock's mark on American letters, even beyond the poetry of Emily Dickinson. Yet geology historian Dennis R. Dean described him as the last geologist who could communicate to the average person, before the specialists took over. He wrote: "So far as America is concerned, Hitchcock is the last significant geological theorist who dabbles, who creates, who imagines, and the grand assurances, the flights of pious imagination, which characterize his works are tragic in their obsolescence. He is, of course, the last American geologist to leave a personal mark upon our creative literature."[136]

Dean cites several allusions to Hitchcock's footprints in great works of literature. In *Moby-Dick*, Herman Melville described Ahab's quarterdeck as "all over dented, like geological stones, with the peculiar mark of his walk."[137] Henry Wadsworth Longfellow also used footprint imagery. He had a personal tie to Hitchcock: His wife's uncle was Samuel Appleton, benefactor of Amherst College's Appleton Cabinet, which housed Hitchcock's footprint collection during the nineteenth century. Longfellow's poem "Psalm of Life" ends with a famous stanza likely inspired by those very tracks in the sandstone. The lines serve as a suitable benediction for Hitchcock himself:

Lives of great men all remind us
We can make our lives sublime,
And, departing, leave behind us
Footprints on the sands of time.

⊰ VINDICATION ⊱

What if Hitchcock clung to his bird theory because he was right? For more than a century his idea was dismissed as merely quaint, but in a sweet twist of science, his bird theory is now considered surprisingly near to the truth. Birds are closely related to dinosaurs. In a sense, both the professor and his detractors have turned out to be right. Hitchcock had footprints but very few bones; Richard Owen in London had bones but very few footprints. Neither had any way of knowing that Hitchcock's birds and Owen's reptiles were actually one and the same.

Hitchcock's bird theory was already in decline in 1864, at the time of his death. Just three years later, when Edward Drinker Cope identified the track makers as dinosaurs, the bird notion truly sank into oblivion. The turnabout would not begin for another century. In the 1960s paleontologist John Ostrom at Yale University started reexamining dinosaur assumptions. He and his former student Robert Bakker argued that dinosaurs were not plodding, cold-blooded reptiles, but rather the smart and agile ancestors of modern birds. In a short paper in the journal *Nature* in 1973, Ostrom first laid out the case that birds had evolved from theropod dinosaurs. Since then, this controversial view has come to be accepted by scientists. Not only are birds descended from dinosaurs, birds *are* dinosaurs.

Feather impressions can be seen on this slab, near the footprint on the right — or so argues a Czech paleontologist. The original image is an albumen photograph from Hitchcock's Supplement to the Ichnology of New England, *published posthumously, in 1865.*

New discoveries continue to be made, including the feathered dino-birds of Liaoning Province in China. Further, in 2005 paleontologists took a closer look at an *Archaeopteryx* specimen from Germany and declared that it had feet designed not for perching, but instead for running on the ground like a dinosaur. *Archaeopteryx* also had a first toe that turned inwards, like *Velociraptor*, which had a long claw for disemboweling its prey. The researchers believe their finding once again strengthens the links between dinosaurs and birds. Other similarities between birds and dinosaurs include hollow bones, hard-shelled eggs, and wishbones. At the moment, scientists are arguing about the origins of feathers, and Hitchcock's tracks have been pulled into the debate. So far, paleontologists have confirmed the presence of feathers in dinosaurs up to 145 million years old. If feathers could be confirmed in Hitchcock's tracks, they would be the earliest ones known, dating back to the early Jurassic, some 200 million years ago.

Arguing for feathers is Martin Kundrat, a paleozoologist from the Czech Republic, who bases his opinion on a particularly fine Amherst College footprint specimen. He contends that impressions near the *Fulicopus* footprints resemble the downy feathers found on young ostriches or emus. These early feather structures would not have been used for flight but perhaps to regulate body temperature. Paleontologist Anthony J. Martin of Emory University in Atlanta disagrees, believing the impressions are merely wrinkles formed in the mud as the dinosaur sat down, wriggling from side to side.

The Appleton Cabinet housed Hitchcock's track collection starting in 1855.

Hitchcock thought he had found evidence of feathers on a different slab. In 1863, only months before he died, he examined a newly obtained specimen of footprints he named *Plesiornis*. Delicate marks in the stone "present so strong a resemblance to the impression of a feather," he wrote, "that I have had it sketched."[138] Some modern paleontologists are skeptical. What Hitchcock saw as feathers, they interpret as a different type of trace, perhaps the trail of an ancient clam.

For all his dedication to the footprints, Hitchcock was weak in one key area: classification. He left footprint taxonomy in a terrible muddle, and later scientists only made it worse. To provide just one example, Hitchcock renamed the big *Eubrontes* footprint four times. He also renumbered the entire track collection no fewer than three times. Emma Rainforth, a professor at Ramapo College in New Jersey, took it upon herself to sort out the mess. Her 2005 doctoral dissertation runs to more than 1,300 pages, including illustrations of the more than one hundred footprint species that Hitchcock described. Rainforth has identified the correct type specimens, those precious specimens that represent new species, and also deciphered all of his footprint names. Her next undertaking will be analyzing the footprints themselves; she will certainly reclassify them. Among forty-eight genera that Hitchcock identified, Rainforth expects to find many that overlap. Ultimately, she expects to end up with about five.

What makes the Connecticut Valley footprints so fascinating is that even now the true identity of the track makers remains a mystery. Hitchcock always hoped to solve the puzzle of the footprints by finding fossil bones, and the great British scientists shared his eagerness. Darwin himself, in his 1845 letter to Hitchcock, wrote, "How sincerely I wish that you may live to discover some of the bones belonging to these gigantic birds."[139] But bones have proven elusive. Apparently, the very conditions that perfectly preserved the footprints were bad for preserving bones. (During the early Jurassic, the Connecticut Valley likely had a somewhat tropical climate, with alternating wet and dry spells. The footprints impressed into the wet mud would have dried hard in the sun.) Further, the New England landscape, with its heavy covering of topsoil and forest, is terrible for fossil hunting.

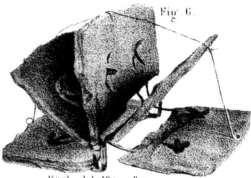

A book from Hitchcock's Stony Library. He made several of these "books," using hinges to join rock pages. This one was his favorite, for it contains fully five pages, showing two tracks passing through five layers of rock.

Using tracks alone, scientists cannot determine much about the appearance of the dinosaur that made them. And so Amherst College geologists faced a tricky challenge when trying to choose a dinosaur for the diorama in the new Museum of Natural History. One possibility was an eight-foot-tall carnivore called *Dilophosaurus*. Its feet nicely fit the big *Eubrontes* tracks in Hitchcock's collections, but its skeletons are found mostly in Arizona, not the Northeast. Another candidate was *Coelophysis*, whose feet are a good match for certain other footprints in the collection. But *Coelophysis* lived at the wrong time, during the Late Triassic, a period that predates Hitchcock's tracks. Given that the Triassic ended in a mass extinction, scientists cannot be sure that *Coelophysis* would have survived to leave its footprints in the Connecticut Valley mud. As for *Anchisaurus*, it seemed a promising candidate, since a good local skeleton exists from the proper time period. Regrettably, its feet aren't a good match for any of the tracks. In the end the geologists decided to use scientists' best approximations and commission a composite dinosaur.

Hitchcock loved the challenge of deciphering the ancient footprints, which he sometimes referred to as hieroglyphics. Today paleontologists continue to test out new hypotheses about the tracks. To prove a point, researchers may spend hours examining clam trails beneath a layer of sediment, or observing footprints left by emus in mats of algae. The difficulty of interpreting the tracks is part of their ongoing appeal.

➤ BEYOND FOOTPRINTS ➤

Despite the toil of transporting enormous sandstone slabs, Hitchcock's footprint collection has been moved several times. As of 1848, the tracks were housed in the Octagon, a building Hitchcock commissioned to hold both the college's natural history collections and its astronomical apparatus. (The attached observatory is long gone.) He loved octagons, and also had one built at his home on South Pleasant Street to display his personal natural history collection. In his architectural taste he was likely influenced by Orson Fowler, the phrenologist and Amherst graduate, who believed octagonal houses superior to square ones for light and ventilation.

When Hitchcock wanted a larger museum, specifically designed for his track collections, he launched one of his fundraising campaigns. In 1855 the Appleton Cabinet ("cabinet" meaning museum) opened its doors. Among its most marvelous exhibits was Hitchcock's Stony Library. The "books" were made from footprints pressed several layers deep into sandstone, with each sandstone layer forming a page. The layers were then bound together with iron hinges.

In 1909 the footprints moved again, this time to the new Biology-Geology building, now called Webster Hall.[140] No longer a college priority, the collection was relegated to the building's basement. Then, about 1950, the footprints were relocated one more time, to the basement of the college's Pratt Museum of Natural History. Except for geology majors, few at the college even knew about the "Track Room," yet it was an unforgettable place, marvelously atmospheric. Dark and cluttered, the room reeked of Victorian-era science. Massive sandstone slabs covered the floor, the tables, even the walls, where they hung from huge metal hooks. At the back of the room stood a white marble bust of Hitchcock, surveying the dusty remnants of his legacy.

With the opening of the college's new Museum of Natural History in 2006, the footprints have emerged from a century of obscurity into the light. In a state-of-the-art exhibition space, the sandstone slabs are cleverly displayed on movable racks. New LED lights provide low-angle illumination, bringing the footprints into dramatic relief. Hitchcock's portrait has been restored and given a place of honor.

Although he badly wanted to be remembered, Hitchcock was also a good sport. Not long before his death, he summed up his entire ichnological endeavor, with all its joys and frustrations, in his *Reminiscences of Amherst College*:

> But though this has been a laborious work, it has been intensely interesting. It was emphatically a new field, and every step I had to feel my way where no one had gone before me; but as I pried open, one after another, the folded leaves of this ancient record, it revealed a marvellous history of the ancient Fauna of this Valley. It was a new branch of Paleontology, whose title-page had scarcely been written in Europe, but I had stumbled upon materials enough almost to fill the volume. Up to this hour I have been trying to spell out the hieroglyphics; and even now, I presume the work is only begun. Success to those who come after me, and may they find in the cabinet which I leave them many curious archives which they shall decipher.

Beyond the footprints, the new natural history museum also highlights other strengths of the college's collections, including its fine skeletons of Ice Age mammals. A saber-toothed cat, a dire wolf, and a mammoth are prominently displayed, along with a mastodon, dramatically illuminated at night through the museum's glass walls.

Important fossils from an early Amherst expedition to South America have also emerged from the Pratt Museum's closets, including the rare skull of an elephantlike *Pyrotherium*. In 1911 a distinguished Amherst biology professor named Frederick Brewster Loomis (Class of 1896) took two students and a cook to Patagonia for the summer. This was a bold adventure, for at the time Patagonia was considered the end of the earth. All told, Loomis took students on more than a dozen digs before he died in 1937 during an expedition to Alaska.

In building a new natural history museum, Amherst has made an extraordinary commitment to preserving its scientific heritage. Most liberal arts colleges in the Northeast dismantled their natural history collections decades ago. Amherst not only held on to its collections but has now opted to make them a campus focal point. In 2005, as the old Pratt Museum was being packed up, photographer Frank Ward found himself drawn to its bones, tracks, feathers, skulls, antlers, and glass eyes. What he discovered comprises the second half of this book. His photographs — wonderfully evocative and unexpected — capture something of the history of the college's collections, and something of their mystery as well.

Cartes de visite, *circa 1860, for Edward and Orra. The latter courtesy of Memorial Hall Museum, Deerfield, Massachusetts.*

✦ CODA ✦

I began this little essay with a letter. And so I will end with one too, written by Hitchcock himself, to the love of his life. It appeared in 1851, as the dedication to *The Religion of Geology*:

To My Beloved Wife

Both gratitude and affection prompt me to dedicate these lectures to you. To your kindness and self-denying labours I have been mainly indebted for the ability and leisure to give any successful attention to scientific pursuits. Early should I have sunk under the pressure of feeble health, nervous despondency, poverty, and blighted hopes, had not your sympathies and cheering counsels sustained me. And during the last thirty years of professional labours, how little could I have done in the cause of science, had you not, in a great measure, relieved me of the cares of a numerous family! Furthermore, while I have described scientific facts with the pen only, how much more vividly have they been portrayed by your pencil! And it is peculiarly appropriate that your name should be associated with mine in any literary effort where the theme is geology; since your artistic skill has done more than my voice to render that science attractive to the young men whom I have instructed. I love especially to connect your name with an effort to defend and illustrate that religion which I am sure is dearer to you than every thing else.

I know that you would forbid this public allusion to your labours and sacrifices, did I not send it forth to the world before it meets your eye. But I am unwilling to lose this opportunity of bearing a testimony which both justice and affection urge me to give. In a world where much is said of female deception and inconstancy, I desire to testify that one man at least has placed implicit confidence in woman, and has not been disappointed. Through many checkered scenes have we passed together, both on the land and sea, at home and in foreign countries; and now the voyage of life is almost ended. The ties of earthly affection, which have so long united us in uninterrupted harmony and happiness, will soon be sundered. But there are ties which death cannot break; and we indulge the hope that by them we shall be linked together and to the throne of God through eternal ages.

In life and in death I abide
Your affectionate husband,

Edward Hitchcock

A LUMINOUS LEGACY: PHOTOGRAPHS *By Frank Ward*

Dear Professor Hitchcock,

Please allow me to introduce myself. I am the photographer who has been inspired by your remarkable collection at Amherst College. You devoted your years on earth to close observation. Thus, I surmise that you had an affinity for photography. I know that you used photographs in your very last book, *Supplement to the Ichnology of New England*, published a year after your death. In this Supplement, you found photography very useful for documenting the footprints you studied. For me, the camera is less a factual instrument of science than a tool through which I can visually explore my own relationship to the world, both natural and cultural. The fossils and footmarks you have left behind have captivated my attention for some time now. You see, sir, these natural specimens are the origin of what, for me, is a "garden of earthly delights."

Let me expand upon this by suggesting that you were the forefather of admirable progeny. The faculty, students, and alumni who follow you at Amherst continue vigorous investigation of the earth's chronological record. In addition to your stone tracks and traces, they have added significant discoveries from the seven continents. Just as you saw implications of Noah's flood in your first fossil discoveries, I see the parade of Noah's beasts in what has been accumulated since your time at Amherst. It is this diversity of visual delights that astounds me. Now, almost one hundred and fifty years after your death, I am approaching these many remnants of natural history with the eye of a portraitist trying to reveal a subject's innermost spirit, be it a moa foot or a taxidermied bluebird.

You, as a scientist, probably suspect that an artist is the least qualified of persons to handle and gaze at your mysterious gatherings. That may be true, but I mean no harm. I am scrutinizing those artifacts for traces of character, for I wish to characterize you and the very collection you initiated. I know that you must have sat for hours alone with your specimens of antiquity. I have done the same. Perhaps, we both began our sessions with a meditation, yours possibly a prayer, mine a contemplation of luminosity. As one of the world's first geologists, and a reverend, you attempted to reconcile Christian doctrine with scientific discoveries. As a colorist and later-day luminist, I celebrate the light and texture of nature. Our experience of these tracks and traces might intersect when we both contemplate the inevitably of time and death incorporated into every aspect of this trove.

I often sat in the vertebrate paleontology classroom amongst primate skeletons, dinosaur skulls, and frogs. It seemed that much of creation shared the room. After the students had midterm and final examinations, the specimens were almost lined up two by two. Admittedly, I sense the evolutionary connections expounded by your contemporary Charles Darwin. Please accept my apologies for bringing up your nemesis, but I am drawn to the platypus, armadillo, and other animals for their many similarities. My other idiosyncrasies include a tendency to photograph what is extant rather than extinct. I have ignored the bulk of your 20,000 collected fossils and have tended toward celebrating what has survived. You will be satisfied to know that the scientists and scholars now at Amherst who are responsible for the preservation of your legacy do not follow my inclination. The faculty and staff at the college know that the extinct is of primary importance. I simply operate under a visual hierarchy; I judge an object's importance by its power of gesture and expression. For instance, I photographed the least bittern because of the way its left leg is held high, like that of a ballet dancer in midpirouette or an archaeologist preparing for a most delicate incision of the shovel.

When the Pratt Museum was being dismantled, I haunted the building's every corridor and cabinet. Granted, my haunting did not approach the echoes of your spirit that imbue almost every stone and bone of the collection. Nonetheless, I consider my hours spent in the museum as a pilgrimage through time. For example, to capture the old Track Room, I sat in the dark with all the lighting extinguished. With your marble bust staring at me, my eyes adjusted to the illumination from two small windows. The dinosaur tracks became infused with light and the dark hall of prehistory took on the aura of an ancient temple. I then opened the shutter for several minutes in an attempt to absorb into my camera that which I experienced.

I photograph in darkness much of the time. I want the objects themselves to provide their own radiance. In silence, I initiate a dialogue with the past. These photographs are the result of this romance. Even though my work is not scientific, it is with the utmost respect, Professor Hitchcock, that I create this body of work. This portfolio is meant as a tribute to you and those who came after you.

Faithfully yours,

The Track Room, which housed Hitchcock's footprint collection from 1950 to 2005.

Noah's Raven slab, the world's first documented fossil footprints, discovered about 1802. The tracks were made by Anomoepus scambus, *a small ornithischian, or "bird-hipped," dinosaur.*

Tracks of Brontozoum validum, *one of the Pioneer Valley's largest dinosaurs.*

Painted footmarks, outlined to emphasize the skeletal morphology.

Moa foot, shown with a petrified tree stump from the 1911 Frederick Loomis expedition to Patagonia. The wooden toes were likely carved by Hitchcock's son Doc.

Moa skeleton. The discovery of the moa, about 1839, bolstered Hitchcock's theory that the local fossil footprints had been made by gigantic ancient birds.

Alcove in the old Pratt Museum, showing (far left and far right) the jaws of an elephantlike Deinotherium. *Hitchcock and Ephraim Brown of Lowell paid $100 for the cast, presenting it to the college in 1862.*

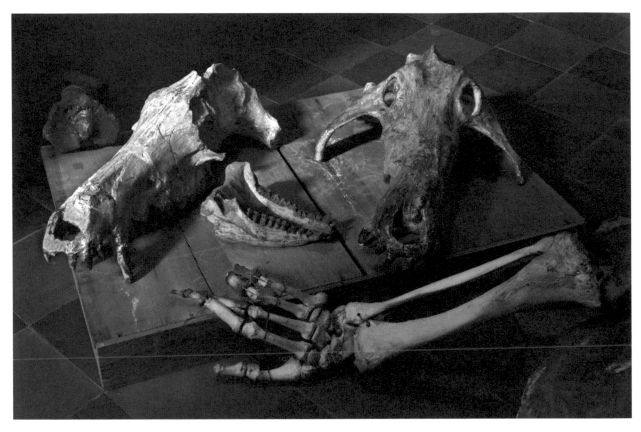

Two entolodont skulls, the right arm of a gorilla, and a mammal's lower jaw.

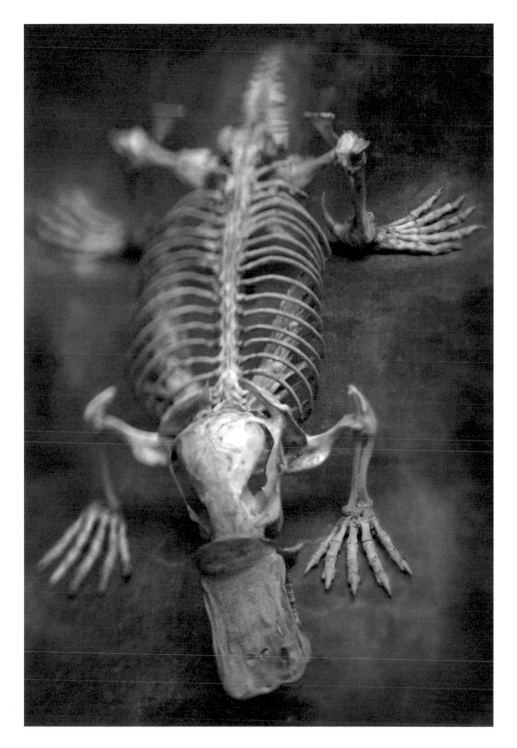

Male platypus skeleton, showing spike on rear foot which in life was attached to a gland filled with poison.

Howler monkey with stromatolite, a fossil created by colonies of microorganisms.

Chimpanzee (left) and orangutan, in the old Paleontology Lab.

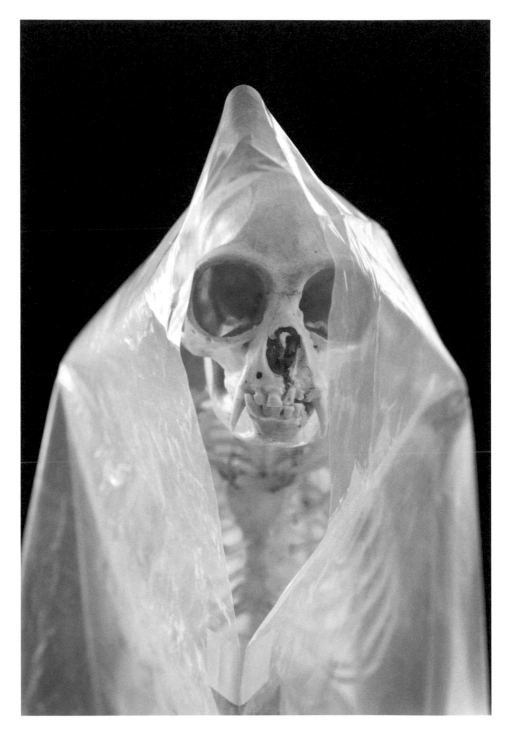

Gibbon, stored in protective plastic sheeting.

Bear with five wooden teeth, possibly carved by Hitchcock's son Doc.

Five lemurs, on a background of Western Massachusetts fossil fish.

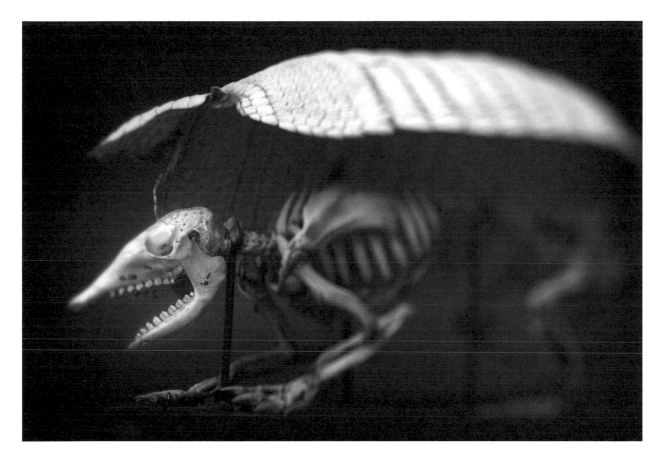

Armadillo, with hinged mount.

Juvenile cebus monkey, resting on a stromatolite.

Cast of skull from a Camarasaurus, *a small sauropod dinosaur.*

Coyote skull, partially exposed, with fur and soft tissue remaining.

Cat with lion, showing their many skeletal similarities.

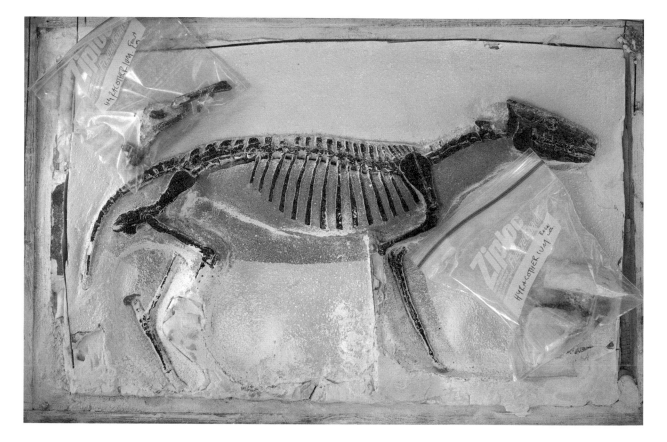

Small early horse, Hyracotherium, *from a display on horse evolution.*

Fox skulls, used in comparative anatomy and introductory biology classes.

Dire wolf, from the La Brea
Tar Pits in Los Angeles.

Hominid skull casts, used in a display on human evolution.

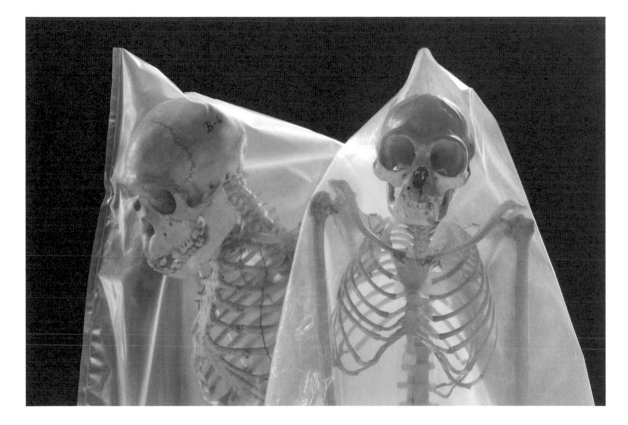

Juvenile chimpanzee and adult gibbon, shrouded for storage.

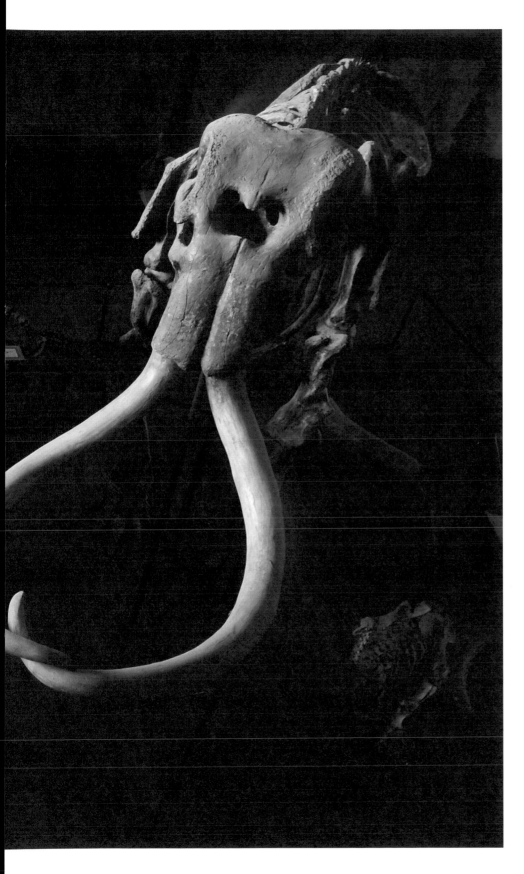

*Mastodon, modern Indian
elephant, and mammoth.
The mastodon was discovered
in 1869 in South Carolina,
and the mammoth in 1925
in Florida.*

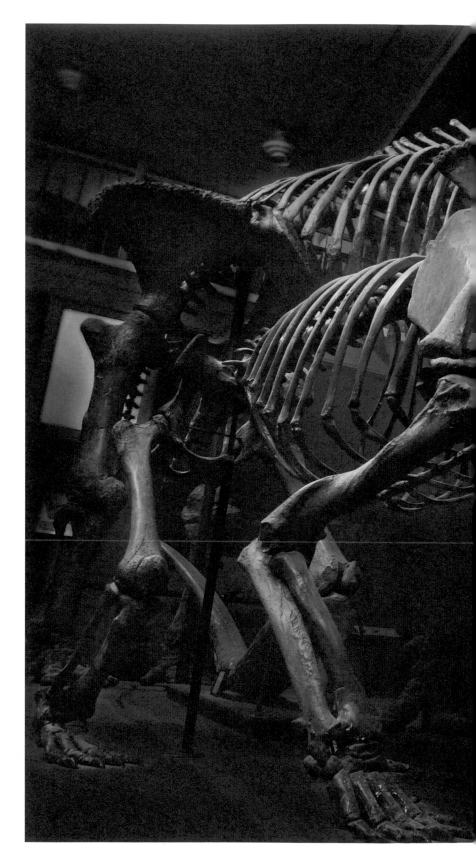

Cave bear, in foreground, an animal that may have competed for habitat with early humans.

Saber-toothed cat, an Ice Age mammal.

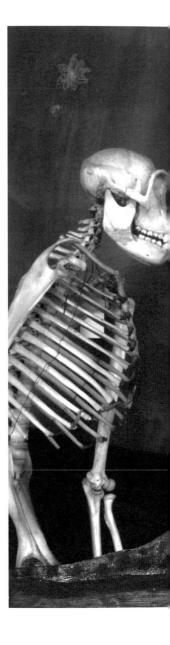

Impala, boxed to protect its fragile ears.

The old Paleontology Lab, showing model of a duck-billed dinosaur made by paleontologist Richard Lull, an expert on Hitchcock's tracks.

Taxidermy collection being prepared for storage. Many African specimens came to the college via missionaries.

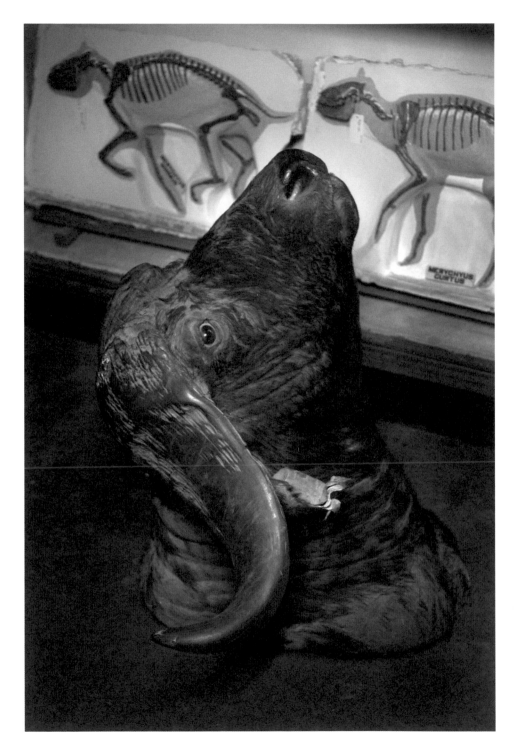

Water buffalo, stored with early sheep called oredonts.

Model of Dunkleosteus, *an ancient armored fish, with paintings of hominids in the background.*

Little brown bat, shown hanging in the cast jaws of a Tyrannosaurus rex.

Fish vertebrae with marine scene painted by Francis Cushing Hall, in the old Pratt Museum.

Dried seahorses, again with background painting by Francis Cushing Hall.

Pufferfish

Taxidermied birds in arched window of the old Pratt Museum, being readied for storage.

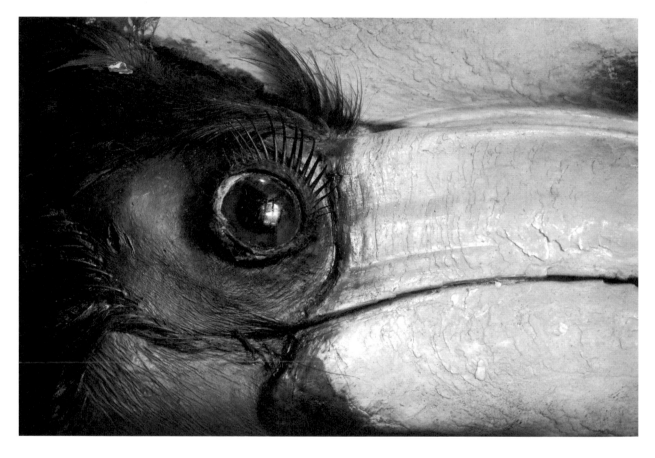

Malabar hornbill.

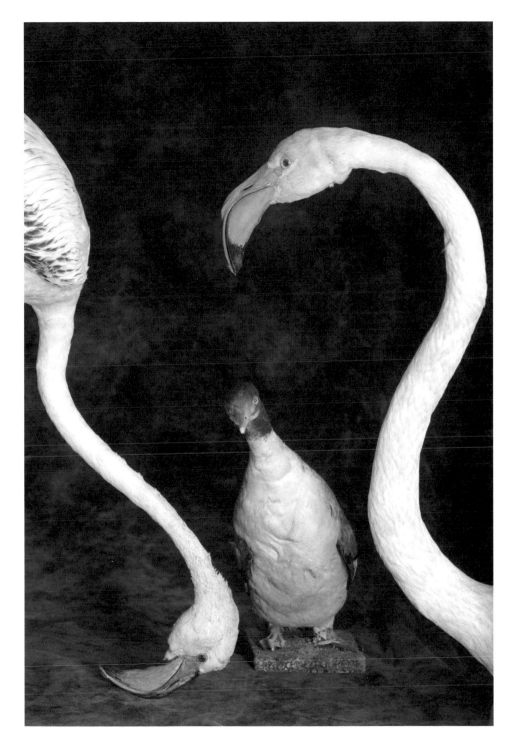

Female merganser and flamingos.

Vulture (left) and eagle, in their storage container.

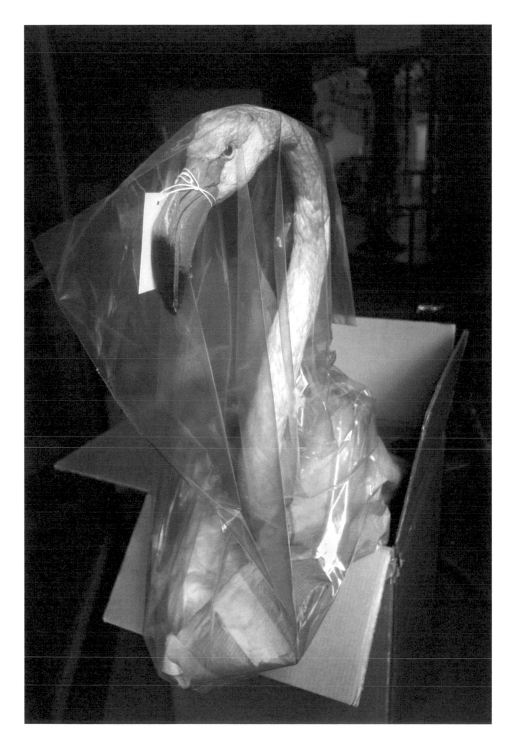

Flamingo, boxed and awaiting repair.

Red-shouldered hawk.

Scarlet ibis, from the bird display in the old Pratt Museum.

Least bittern.

Bluebird, waiting to be put into storage.

Nineteen arrows from the Orinoco River region of South America, likely collected by Amherst-educated missionaries.

Bones of miscellaneous modern mammals.

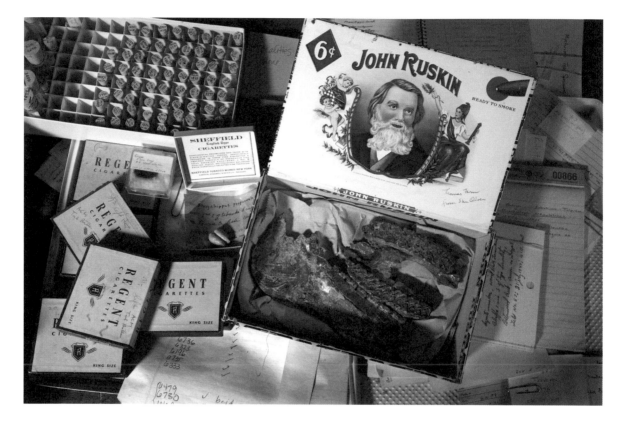

Cigar and cigarette boxes used for storing small specimens in the old Paleontology Lab.

Wild boar tusks.

Damaged impalas.

FRANK WARD'S MEDITATION ON NATURAL HISTORY

And gather me into the artifice of eternity.
— William Butler Yeats, "Sailing to Byzantium"

Frank Ward's pictures of the Amherst College Museum of Natural History specimens are, to my knowledge, a unique modern achievement in this often-attempted subject. Rejecting the ready-made surrealism of the lifelike nonliving thing in real or lifelike settings (such as waxwork figures and store window mannequins), Ward has worked faithfully within the documentary style. The fiction of that style, for Ward and all true documentary workers, is that allegiance is to the thing itself, to information, and that whatever visual effects the pictures have are the result of technical properties of the instrument or materials.

Consider the red-shouldered hawk of page 100. Its face is precisely rendered down to the finest feathers (which reveal that some birds have eyelashes), the beak down to the subtlest patches of color — details we don't usually notice in display case specimens. But the head and wing are only roughly generalized. This clash of visual styles is, we feel, an unavoidable result of the lens being so close to the subject and so sharply focused on its face.

However, considered as itself, the wing is a uniquely shaped form within the frame and a ground against which are figured varied patches of color and undulating lines that set up brief patterns of black, orange, silver, and gold. In contrast to the head, precise as a drawing with a sharp hard pencil, the wing is a sketch, almost abstract, as though Ward laid it in and modeled it with pastels at the ends of his fingertips. That this is no accident is borne out by his pictures of a platypus skeleton, a bear's mouth, a coyote's skull, and others with similar abrupt transitions between the contour drawing and the rough, gestural sketch.

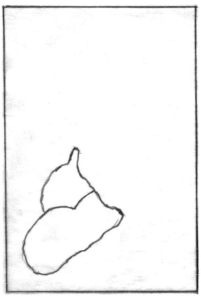

Consider *Damaged Impalas* (opposite). After the charm of the animals' tenderness subsides, after we find the damaged parts and see the different shapes and lengths of the horns, we come upon the necks, whose contour lines (roughly traced) you see at right.

In the manner of all artists in this style, he begins his pictures as invitations to see and understand the moment and ends them as revelations of form.

The pictures' strangeness comes from our seeing these specimens as we never see them in life. It is as though Ward has taken us into the display cases, across the diorama's plush ropes, and down into the museum's storage vaults and caves. However, his pictures' power comes from his creations of forms, from which he constructs his compositions which are, in turn, observations of and hymns to the fact and mystery of existence as represented by the presence of these specimens in space and time.

Whether they died millions of years ago or by a modern hunter's gun, the animals that became or provided these specimens began a second life in time as we experience it when they arrived at the Amherst College Museum of Natural History and were cleaned, articulated, measured, weighed, classified, cataloged, drawn, photographed. Then time stopped again for them as, in their display cases and dioramas, they became symbols of fixed moments in the museum's organization of millennia.

Fixed, that is, until the interval between the closing of the old Pratt Museum of Natural History and the opening of the new. Detached from their original places they were moved here and there, wrapped in or combined with materials invented long after their deaths (two Ziploc bags taped to a fossilized *Small Early Horse*, page 70), tumbled together with others of their species or, as in the picture of the simian skeleton and the little dinosaur model in front of the paleontology room's blackboard (*The Old Paleontology Lab*, page 83) brought into contact with other species (including ours: "Clean up archaeology room" the blackboard reads) and, indeed, with other eras, to form improbable evolutionary schemas.

Out of this period of the specimens' uprootedness Ward has created poetic order. Varying from picture to picture, it spans comedy — as in *Chimpanzee and Orangutan* (page 61): two skeletons talking over fragmentary notes on a blackboard; mystery — as *Little Brown Bat* (page 89), in which the animal, caught in a plastic bag, seems suspended between the teeth of a giant mouth, or in *Five Lemurs* (page 64), in which five small skulls on a cave ledge seem to sit in judgment, but on whom or for what we cannot tell; parody — as in *Fish Vertebrae* (page 90), in which it is ambiguous as to whether the real fish mocks the painted crabs or vice versa). *Two Entolodont Skulls* (page 58), in which the hand looks like it is pushing the skulls away, seems to capture a moment in time. And *Fox Skulls* (page 71) is a modern three-dimensional realization of steel-point engravings found in the great nineteenth-century naturalist Louis Agassiz's works on the variation of form in body parts within a single species.

With this last observation we are at a source of these pictures' power. Ward has not only brought the specimens to life within the world of his original forms and compositions. He has also pictured them within the terms of several centuries of Western art. We have already seen his sketching, which resonates with old master drawings and nineteenth-century lithography. Parts of pictures, like the beak in *Malabar Hornbill* (page 96), and whole pictures, like *Bear with Five*

Wooden Teeth (page 63), closely approximate the conditions of abstract painting. *Nineteen Arrows* (page 104) resonates with serial painting and the stripe paintings of Frank Stella. With *Bones* (page 105) we are at once in the realm of Donald Judd and minimalism and Joseph Cornell and late surrealism. And in picture after picture we see Ward's skillful handling of one of the most ancient means of visual art: motif and variation.

Ward's handling of the documentary foundation of his style has been faithful to the nature of these specimens as representatives of the evolution of species over slow geophysical time. It has also shown much that happened to them during their brief second existence in diurnal time as they awaited the move to their new quarters. His handling of form and his knowledge of pictorial tradition, however, have positioned them in the timeless realm of art.

— Ben Lifson
Photography critic, historian, and teacher

NOTES

1. Edward Hitchcock (hereafter "EH"), *Supplement to the Ichnology of New England. A Report to the Government of Massachusetts, in 1863* (Boston: Wright & Potter, 1865), 33.

2. Charles Darwin to EH, 6 November 1845, Edward and Orra White Hitchcock Papers (hereafter EH and OWH Papers), (Box 3, Folder 8, original in vault), Archives and Special Collections, Amherst College Library.

3. John Servos, historian of science at Amherst College, comments that Hitchcock "was known, of course, for his collection of footprints, but his other contributions to geology were at least as impressive. The greatest problem of his era was constructing a universal stratigraphical column — that is, correlating rocks found in various parts of the world according to their temporal relationships with one another. This work began in Europe during the late eighteenth century and progressed rapidly in the nineteenth — leading by about 1850 to a sequence that is the basis of our classification. This was one reason Lyell was so interested in Hitchcock's work. Hitchcock's studies provided some of the data necessary for establishing links between the British strata and those of the American Northeast."

4. Steven Sauter, Coordinator of Education at Amherst College's Museum of Natural History, suggests that EH's bird theory reflects Ockham's Razor, the principle proposed in the fourteenth century by William of Ockham, *"Pluralitas non est ponenda sine necessitate,"* or, "Entities should not be multiplied unnecessarily." In other words, the simplest or most obvious explanation should be preferred until proven wrong.

5. EH, *Reminiscences of Amherst College, Historical, Scientific, Biographical and Autobiographical: Also, of Other and Wider Life Experiences* (Northampton, Mass.: Bridgman & Childs, 1863), 87.

6. Ibid.

7. EH, "Report on Ichnolithology, or Fossil Footmarks, with a Description of several New Species, and the Coprolites of Birds, from the valley of the Connecticut River...," *American Journal of Science* 47, no. 2 (1844): 298.

8. EH, "Ornithichnology. Description of the Foot marks of Birds, (Ornithichnites) on new Red Sandstone in Massachusetts," *American Journal of Science* 29, no. 2 (1836): 308.

9. See letter from Benjamin Silliman to EH, 6 August 1835, in response to a letter from EH that has been lost: "I am much gratified that you are seriously at work upon the turkey tracks or birds tracks of whatever kind they may be." Silliman, a geologist and chemist at Yale, was EH's mentor. He was also founding editor of the *American Journal of Science and Arts*. (The name was later shortened to *American Journal of Science*, as it appears in these notes.)

10. Dennis R. Dean, "Hitchcock's Dinosaur Tracks," *American Quarterly* 21 (1969): 641, footnote 6.

11. See letter from EH to Charles Lyell, 17 December 1843, courtesy of Department of Special Collections, Edinburgh University Library, Scotland: "The opinion that these tracks were those of birds, was a common one among the quarrymen, who usually called them *turkey tracks.*"

12. EH, "Ornithichnology," 317.

13. EH, "Report on Ichnolithology," 295.

14. EH, untitled poem, *The Knickerbocker* 8 (1836): 751.

15. Ibid., 752, first footnote.

16. EH, from his unpublished diary notes, spanning the years 1829 to 1864 (hereafter "Diary"). The diary, which was later given page numbers, is found in the EH and OWH Papers at Amherst College Archives and Special Collections, Amherst College Library. This quotation from 3 November 1855, 278 (Box 19, Folder 5).

17. Suzanne L. Flynt, "Orra White Hitchcock's Early Years," in *Orra White Hitchcock,* exhibition catalog, Christina M. Cohen, ed. (Deerfield, Mass.: Deerfield Academy, 1992), 2.

18. Although EH never attended college, he did receive an unsolicited Master of Arts degree from Yale in 1818, at age twenty-five, for his informal studies with Benjamin Silliman. In 1840 he received an honorary Doctor of Laws degree from Harvard.

19. Eugene C. Worman, "Orra White Hitchcock's Amherst Years," in *Orra White Hitchcock,* 9. Of the play, EH wrote, "A juvenile production which should not have been published. But it contains some real poetry, and was loudly called for by the rural population before whom it was acted with much success." *Reminiscences of Amherst College,* 388.

20. John Servos notes that this unpuritanical attitude toward courtship was fairly typical of the era.

21. EH to Orra White Hitchcock, n.d., EH and OWH Papers (Box 5, Folder 31).

22. EH to Orra White Hitchcock, n.d., EH and OWH Papers (Box 5 Folder 31).

23. Thanks to Steven Sauter for this insight.

24. See *A Painted Herbarium, The Life and Art of Emily Hitchcock Terry (1838–1921)* (Minneapolis: University of Minnesota Press, 1992).

25. EH Diary, 30 March 1840, 65 (Box 19, Folder 3).

26. Notes his Diary, on p. 71: "In my sickness three years ago [1839] I was favored with some peculiar optical delusions which gave a deep interest to my sickness.... I was in fact dreaming while perfectly awake. I had only to close my eyes at any time in order to have pass before me a continued series of splendid visions which I could examine & describe to an amanuensis with as much coolness as I could a series of paintings in an artist's collection." (Box 19, Folder 3)

27. Edward Hitchcock, *Dyspepsy Forestalled and Resisted: or Lectures on Diet, Regimen, and Employment*, 2nd ed. (Amherst, Mass.: J. S. & C. Adams, 1831), 305.

28. Ibid., 2.

29. EH Diary, 26 August 1832, 32 (Box 19, Folder 3).

30. Ibid., 33.

31. Ibid., 34.

32. EH, *History of a Zoological Temperance Convention, Held in Central Africa* (Fitchburg, Mass.: George Trask, 1864), 39–40.

33. EH Diary, 36.

34. Notes John Servos, "Hitchcock's work as a state geologist was important in creating precedents for surveys of many other states. He delivered what he promised on time and within budget, and established patterns both for managing the work and publishing results that were emulated as other states organized surveys later in the nineteenth century. These state surveys were the major investment in science made by government in the middle part of the nineteenth century and laid the foundation for later federal surveys, including the U.S. Geological Survey (organized in 1879)."

35. EH's geologic map of Massachusetts was not updated until B. K. Emerson of Amherst College published a full-color bedrock map in 1916, under the auspices of the United States Geological Survey. See Arthur A. Socolow, ed., *The State Geological Surveys: A History* ([Grand Forks?], N.D.: Association of American State Geologists, 1988), 221. Aerial photography of the state would not begin until 1936.

36. EH Diary, 9 February 1834, 44 (Box 19, Folder 3).

37. Ibid., 48.

38. EH Diary, 28 December 1834, 51 (Box 19, Folder 3).

39. Editors, "Ornithichnites of the Connecticut River Sandstones and the Dinornis of New Zealand," *American Journal of Science* 45, no. 1 (1843): 177.

40. Letters from Darwin, Mantell, and Owen are found in the Amherst College archives. Letters to EH from Lyell are housed at Edinburgh University Library, Scotland.

41. EH, "Bibliographical Notices," *American Journal of Science* 48, no. 1 (1844): 201.

42. Ibid.

43. Ibid.

44. Stephen Jay Gould, *The Lying Stones of Marrakech* (New York: Three Rivers Press, 2000), 152.

45. Charles Lyell, *Travels in North America; with Geological Observations on the United States, Canada, and Nova Scotia*, vol. 1 (London: John Murray, 1845), 251.

46. Ibid., 254.

47. See letter from Mantell to James Deane, in "Ornithichnites of the Connecticut River Sandstones,"184.

48. Thanks to John Servos for this idea.

49. Darwin to EH, 6 November 1845.

50. Ibid.

51. EH to Lyell, 17 December 1843.

52. Owen to EH, 30 August 1844, EH and OWH Papers (Box 3, Folder 30).

53. Owen to Silliman, in "Ornithichnites of the Connecticut River Sandstones,"186–187.

54. Ibid., 187.

55. Ibid., 188.

56. EH to Lyell, 17 December 1843.

57. EH, *Religious Truth, Illustrated from Science, in Addresses and Sermons on Special Occasions* (Boston: Phillips, Sampson, 1857), 169.

58. L. N. Fowler, "Phrenological Descriptions of Prof. Edward Hitchcock," 13 May 1847, Phrenological Cabinet, New York, EH & OWH Papers (Box 1, Folder 2).

59. Mantell to EH, 11 July 1845, EH & OWH Papers (Box 3, Folder 24): "I have hunted over a few grains of your coprolites in the hope of detecting infusoria with the microscope, but no traces of organization appear." Also, Owen to EH, 30 August 1844.

60. William Buckland, "On the Discovery of Coprolites, or Fossil Faeces, in the Lias at Lyme Regis, and in other Formations," *Transactions of the London Geological Society*, 2nd series, part 3 (1835): 223–236.

61. Buckland, *Geology and Mineralogy Considered with Reference to Natural Theology,"* vol. 1, Bridgewater Treatises 6 (London: W. Pickering, 1836), 201–202.

62. EH, "Report on Ichnolithology," 308.

63. Ibid., 310.

64. Ibid.

65. Ibid., 309.

66. Ibid., 310.

67. Owen to EH, 30 August 1844.

68. Ibid.

69. EH, Geology lecture notes, n.p., EH and OWH Papers (Box 10, Folder 10).

70. EH, *Report on the Geology, Mineralogy, Botany, and Zoology of Massachusetts* (Amherst: J. S. and C. Adams, 1833), 142.

71. Louis Agassiz published his great Ice Age book, *Etudes sur les Glaciers* ("Study on Glaciers") in 1840.

72. Lyell, *Travels in North America*, 252.

73. Climate change is not the only reason why the Connecticut Valley was once much warmer. During the early Jurassic period, the landmass itself was located closer to the equator.

74. EH, *Elementary Geology*, 8th ed. (New York: Mark H. Newman, 1847), 224.

75. Ibid., 220.

76. Hitchcock believed the Connecticut Valley had once consisted of a series of basins where the river widened out, forming "narrow lakes or ponds." Yet he stopped short of concluding that the entire valley had once been a lake. According to Richard Little of Greenfield Community College, EH was misled in part because the land was no longer flat, as a lakebed should be. Instead, it was tilted, slanted downwards from north to south. To EH, this looked like a typical riverbed, sloping toward the sea, but in fact the lakebed had tilted due to "rebound," the rising of the land as the glacial ice melted. Rebounding was higher in the north than in the south.

77. Alice M. Walker, unnamed article, *The Springfield Union*, 25 September 1904, typescript, Buildings and Grounds Collection (Box 5, Folder 46), Archives and Special Collections, Amherst College Library.

78. Marion Lansing, ed., *Mary Lyon Through Her Letters* (Boston: Books, Inc., 1937), 164.

79. EH, *Religious Truth*, 354.

80. Ibid., 366.

81. Thomas H. Johnson, ed., *Emily Dickinson: Selected Letters* (Cambridge: Harvard University Press, 1986), 21.

82. Nina Baym, *American Women of Letters and the Nineteenth-Century Sciences* (New Brunswick, N.J.: Rutgers University Press, 2002), 133–134.

83. Richard Sewall, *The Life of Emily Dickinson* (New York: Farrar, Straus and Giroux, 1980), 343.

84. EH, *Religious Lectures on Peculiar Phenomena in the Four Seasons* (Boston: Crosby, Nichols, Lee, 1861), 104.

85. Sewall, *The Life of Emily Dickinson*, 355. Emily Dickinson's poem, number 1261, is quoted from *The Poems of Emily Dickinson*, R.W. Franklin, ed. (Cambridge: Harvard University Press, 1998), 493.

86. EH, *The Highest Use of Learning: An Address Delivered at His Inauguration to the Presidency of Amherst College* (Amherst: Trustees of Amherst College, 1845), 9. Hitchcock also wrote a charming lecture proclaiming the superiority of science over literature, "The Wonders of Science Compared with the Wonders of Romance." He writes: "My object is to convince my hearers, that here [in science] is a far wider and nobler field, and a profusion of more delicious fruit, and sparkling gems, than fiction can offer." *Religious Truth, Illustrated from Science*, p. 135.

87. EH, *The Highest Use of Learning*, 30.

88. EH, *Elementary Geology*, 1847 ed., 96.

89. As EH states in his 1847 textbook, p. 96: "We learn…that in the earlier periods of the world, the less complex and less perfect tribes of animals and plants greatly predominated, and that the more perfect species became more and more numerous up to the creation of the present races."

90. For support, EH quoted English paleontologist William Buckland. In 1836, Buckland had made a valiant effort to reconcile geology and theology, in his book *Geology and Mineralogy Considered with Reference to Natural Theology*, part of an important series known as the Bridgewater Treatises. Examining everything from minerals to fossilized plants, Buckland had sought to show evidence of an intelligent Creator.

91. EH, *Elementary Geology*, 1863 ed., 270.

92. Ibid.

93. EH Diary, 15 August 1847, 137 (Box 19, Folder 4).

94. Ibid., 138.

95. See letter from EH to Benjamin Silliman, 16 October 1852, EH and OWH Papers (Box 5, Folder 19; original at the Historical Society of Pennsylvania).

96. John Servos points out that while evolution was accepted fairly quickly by most scientists, "the adequacy of natural selection as a creative force remained controversial until the 1930s."

97. EH, *Elementary Geology*, 1863 ed., 270.

98. Francis Bacon, quoted in Charles Coulston Gillispie, *Genesis and Geology: The Impact of Scientific Discoveries Upon Religious Beliefs in the Decades Before Darwin* (New York: Harper & Brothers, 1959), 31.

99. For this statement, I beg indulgence from Galileo, who was Catholic, and my friend John Kleiner at Williams College.

100. Gillispie, *Genesis and Geology*, 223.

101. Ibid.

102. Hitchcock describes in *The Religion of Geology*,

p. 26, the intellectual shift that occurred in the wake of Copernicus, even by Christian believers: "Not only has the motion of the earth been established, but it has been made equally obvious that this truth is in entire harmony with the language of Scripture; so that neither the infidel nor the Christian ever suspect, on this ground, any collision between the two records."

103. EH, *The Religion of Geology and Its Connected Sciences* (Glasgow: William Collins, 1865), 120.

104. EH, "Report on Ichnolithology," 310.

105. EH, *The Religion of Geology*, 46.

106. Hitchcock here embraces "gap theory," the idea that vast periods of time elapsed between the first and second verses of the Bible. Other theologians disagreed, including Hitchcock's mentor at Yale, Benjamin Silliman, who believed that each day of Creation lasted thousands of years.

107. EH, *The Religion of Geology and Its Connected Sciences*, 2nd ed. (Boston: Crosby, Nichols, Lee, 1860), xvi.

108. EH, "An Attempt to Discriminate and Describe the Animals That Made the Fossil Footmarks of the United States, and Especially of New England," *Memoirs of American Arts and Sciences* 7 (1848): 250–251.

109. EH, *Elementary Geology*, 1865 ed., 327.

110. Roswell Field, "Ornithichnites, or tracks resembling those of Birds," *American Journal of Science,* 2nd series, 29, no. 87 (1860): 362.

111. Ibid., 363.

112. In his 1863 edition of *Elementary Geology*, p. 309, Hitchcock wrote that the Connecticut Valley footprints were probably from "the equivalent of the lower part of the oolite, say liassic, or possibly it is the upper part of the trias." (In other words, he dated the tracks to early Jurassic or late Triassic periods.) Scientists now place the tracks in the early Jurassic, about 200 million years ago.

113. EH, *Supplement to the Ichnology of New England*, 33.

114. Ibid., 37.

115. Ibid., 30.

116. Ibid., 31.

117. Ibid.

118. Ibid., 37.

119. Ibid., 32.

120. Ibid., 33.

121. James Dwight Dana, quoted in EH's "New Facts and Conclusions respecting the Fossil Footmarks of the Connecticut Valley," *American Journal of Science,* 2nd series, 36, no. 106 (1863): 57.

122. Jeffries Wyman, as quoted by Hitchcock, in Richard Swann Lull, *Triassic Life of the Connecticut Valley*, revised ed. (Hartford: Printed for the State Geological and Natural History Survey, 1953), 99.

123. Ibid.

124. Owen, quoted by Edward Hitchcock Jr., in Appendix A to EH's *Supplement to the Ichnology of New England*, 40.

125. Edward Drinker Cope, "An Account of the Extinct Reptiles which Approached the Birds," *Proceedings of the Academy of Natural Sciences of Philadelphia* 19 (1867): 234–235.

126. EH Diary, 7 January 1860, 348 (Box 19, Folder 5).

127. Ibid., 349.

128. Ibid., 350.

129. John Servos comments: "It is interesting to note that Hitchcock assumes that the collection is his to give away. This attitude…is quite typical of the period. Professors generally received little support for original investigations (Hitchcock made his collections using state and personal funds) and were generally not evaluated on the basis of such accomplishments. Research and scholarship were, in other words, private affairs, and hence the fruit of such work was considered personal property. This attitude would change only slowly in the decades after the Civil War."

130. EH Diary, 29 April 1860, 355 (Box 19, Folder 5).

131. Worman, "Orra White Hitchcock's Amherst Years," 9.

132. EH Diary, 6 June 1863, 446 (Box 19, Folder 5).

133. Johnson, ed., *Emily Dickinson: Selected Letters*, 183.

134. EH Diary, 4 January 1864, 465 (Box 19, Folder 5).

135. Sewall, *The Life of Emily Dickinson*, 355.

136. Dean, "Hitchcock's Dinosaur Tracks," 644.

137. Herman Melville, *Moby-Dick* (Berkeley: University of California Press, 1979), 163.

138. EH, *Supplement to the Ichnology of New England*, 36.

139. Darwin to EH, 6 November 1845.

140. Thanks to Peter Nelson at Archives and Special Collections, Amherst College Library, for tracing the elusive history of the track collection.

This image, Triumphal Arch of Summer, *is taken from Hitchcock's charming book* Religious Lectures on Peculiar Phenomena in the Four Seasons. *It shows a rainbow over the buildings of Amherst College, which with a certain artistic license are clustered together. Johnson Chapel is clearly visible, as well as the old astronomical observatory once attached to the Octagon.*

A BRIEF EDWARD HITCHCOCK CHRONOLOGY

1793   Born in Deerfield, Massachusetts, on May 24.

1814   Suffers an attack of mumps that leaves his eyes permanently weakened, and abandons his dream of studying astronomy at Harvard.

1818   Receives a Master of Arts degree from Yale College, based on informal studies with his mentor, Benjamin Silliman, a geologist and chemist.

1819   Studies theology, also at Yale.

1821   Marries Orra White, a teacher at Deerfield Academy. Becomes minister of Congregational Church in Conway, Massachusetts. Amherst College founded.

1825   Joins faculty of Amherst College, teaching chemistry and natural history.

1830   Appointed first state geologist of Massachusetts.

1833   Publishes his *Report on the Geology, Mineralogy, Botany, and Zoology of Massachusetts*, establishing his scientific reputation.

1836   Publishes his first paper on fossil footprints, founding the branch of science called Ichnology. He attributes the footprints to gigantic ancient birds.

1839   Richard Owen in London predicts the existence of a gigantic extinct bird in New Zealand, later called the moa. This bolsters Hitchcock's bird theory.

1840   Publishes his textbook *Elementary Geology*, which goes through thirty-one editions.

1841   Visited by Charles Lyell, the great English geologist, who views the footprints.

1842   Owen names the order *Dinosauria*, from which the word "dinosaur" is coined.

1845–54 Serves as president of Amherst College and saves the college from bankruptcy.

1851   Publishes *Religion of Geology*, reconciling the latest science with the Bible.

1858   Publishes *Ichnology of New England*, his magnum opus on fossil footprints.

1859   Darwin publishes *Origin of Species*.

1864   Dies on February 27, at age seventy.

AUTHOR'S ACKNOWLEDGMENTS

My essay in this book grew out of Steve Sauter's uncanny ability to bring Edward Hitchcock to life. Steve gave fabulously inspired tours of the Track Room in the old Pratt Museum — that quirky, evocative, and very Victorian place we both loved. As this project took shape, Steve proved unfailingly generous with his time and his ideas, and I am eternally indebted to him for his help.

Two other people were instrumental in making this book a reality, Michael Kiefer and Stacey Schmeidel. Michael, as the college's Chief Advancement Officer, kindly gave the idea a nudge from the administration side. Stacey, the college's Director of Public Affairs, was the book's main booster, and I cannot thank her enough for guiding the project along, from start to finish. Also essential was Su Auerbach, the college's Design Director, who devoted her time, her enthusiasm, and her wonderful eye, apparent on every page. Copy editor Chris Jerome read the text with care (I would write "great care," only Chris caught my overuse of the word *great*) and saved many sentences from clumsiness.

John Servos, Professor of History at the college, generously agreed to read my manuscript, earning my deep gratitude. As a distinguished historian of science, he knew the context of Hitchcock's story in a way that I did not. I first enlisted his aid when trying to identify a mysterious stone vessel pictured in the background of a Hitchcock portrait. Someone had suggested it might be an early seismic detector. John looked closely and correctly concluded that it was a birdbath! A few months later, his comments on my manuscript prompted me to send him this note: "In my entire 25-year writing life, I don't think anyone has ever read a draft of mine with the thoroughness that you did." His suggestions led to numerous corrections and clarifications in the text, and I have entered some of his comments as footnotes because they are so illuminating.

Peter Crowley, Professor of Geology and Director of the Museum of Natural History, was enthusiastic about Curious Footprints from the outset, and kindly lent his full support. Kate Wellspring, the museum's Collections Manager, was not only incredibly generous with her time and her knowledge, but also unfailingly cheerful. Karen Searcy, curator of the herbarium at the University of Massachusetts, Amherst, generously took the time to show me fascinating plant specimens collected by Hitchcock in the 1820s and formerly housed at Amherst College.

At the college library's Archives and Special Collections, Peter Nelson was nearly heroic in tracking down facts that eluded me, producing high-resolution images, and checking over my work. Daria D'Arienzo, Head of Archives, went out of her way to make this project run smoothly. Staff members Marian Walker and Margaret Dakin were endlessly patient and helpful.

Two old friends kindly read and improved my prose, John Kleiner, my Amherst classmate, and Robert Karjel, a former Copeland Fellow at the college. My father, Thomas Pick '52, conveyed to me his enthusiasm for both the history of science and for Amherst College. My mother, Sue Novitsky Pick, gave me my love of words. My husband, Lawrence Douglas, listened to my ramblings and helped me make sense of things. As a much-loved professor at the college, he follows in the best tradition of Hitchcock. My sons, Jacob and Milo, did what they always do: they made everything matter.

— N. P.

PHOTOGRAPHER'S ACKNOWLEDGMENTS

What began as informal visits to the Pratt Museum developed into a full-blown photography project through the openness, generosity, and expertise of Collections Manager Kate Wellspring. Steve Sauter, the Coordinator of Education, was a tremendous help, offering his depth of understanding of the collection's history. Professor Peter Crowley, the museum Director, expressed a commitment to my project from the beginning. I would also like to thank the rest of the faculty and staff affiliated with the natural history collection: Professor Tekla Harms, Professor Jack Cheney, Professor Whitey Hagadorn, Professor Ed Belt, Professor Margery Coombs, Department Coordinator Jackie Newberry, and Technician Bill Slocombe.

Michael Kiefer, Amherst College's Chief Advancement Officer, was invaluable for his continuous support of the book idea. I am grateful to Stacey Schmeidel, Director of Public Affairs, who shepherded the project through its many stages. Design Director Su Auerbach was inspirational in her vision and understanding of my photographs. I especially want to thank President Tony Marx for his enthusiasm and imagination in seeing this book to fruition.

Many people provided creative and technical assistance for this project: Ben Lifson, my friend and mentor from Bard College, brought a specificity of vision to my photographs that led to the improvement of almost every image. A special thank you to Paula Gillen at *The New Yorker* for sharing my excitement and encouraging me to continue. I would also like to thank Robert Aller, Christopher Lizon, and Stan Sherer, all friends and photographers, for their creative expertise and artistic vision. Key assistance for locating additional Edward Hitchcock material was provided by Daria D'Arienzo and her knowledgeable staff at Amherst College's Archives and Special Collections; Karen Cardinal, Stephen Fisher, and Tim Gilfillin at the Mead Art Museum; and Curator Suzanne Flynt at the Memorial Hall Museum in Deerfield.

I am most deeply indebted to my wife and editor, Vivian Leskes; my children, Tobey and Caleb; and my parents, Frank and Florence Ward, for their unwavering love and support.

— F. W.

BIOGRAPHIES

NANCY PICK graduated from Amherst College in 1983, when women at the school were still a novelty. A former journalist for the *Baltimore Sun*, she now works as a freelance writer. She has written about Edward Hitchcock for *Gastronomica* and the *Boston Globe Magazine*. Her first book, *The Rarest of the Rare: Stories Behind the Treasures at the Harvard Museum of Natural History* (HarperCollins, 2004), was named one of the twenty best science books of the year by *Discover* magazine. She lives in Sunderland, Massachusetts, under the shadow of Mount Sugarloaf.

FRANK WARD was the Amherst College Photographer for twenty-two years. His photographs have appeared in the *New York Times*, *Dance* magazine and *Oprah* magazine. He has received several grants, including a Packard Foundation/Center for Balkan Development grant to photograph in Kosovo, and a National Endowment for the Arts/New England Foundation for the Arts grant for his work in Holyoke, Massachusetts. His photographs have been exhibited widely, including at OK Harris Gallery in New York; Palazzo Reale, Milan, Italy; and the Institute for North American Culture, Santiago, Chile. He has an MFA from Bard College and has taught photography at Amherst College and Smith College. Currently, he is Assistant Professor of Photography at Holyoke Community College.